BRAINSPOTTING WITH CHILDREN AND ADOLESCENTS

BRAINSPOTTING WITH CHILDREN AND ADOLESCENTS

An attuned treatment approach for effective brain-body healing

MONIKA BAUMANN

Mag. Monika Baumann

Published by
Monika Baumann
© 2020 Vienna

Serravagasse 6/2, 1140 Vienna
brainspottingkids@gmail.com
brainspottingaustria@gmail.com

First Printing, 2020

ISBN 978-3-9504927-8-1
www.brainspotting-kids.com

For my husband José Luis and my three daughters,
Carolina, Claudia, and Cristina.
They not only support me, they believe in me.

***

CONTENTS

Acknowledgement

As a representative for the mutually supportive Brainspotting community, I would like to thank **Dr. David Grand**, the founder of Brainspotting, and **Dr. Martha Jacobi**, my friend, and Brainspotting colleague.

Dr. Martha Jacobi not only opened doors for me when I attended my first Brainspotting Trainers training in New York, she also opened doors to a wonderful friendship and teamwork in which we continue to help each other. As soon as I entered her apartment, we sat at her kitchen table and exchanged our experiences in Brainspotting work. Very quickly, we realized how enthusiastic and successful we both had been in using Brainspotting with children and teenagers in different locations in the world. Dr. Jacobi and I maintain a lively exchange regarding work with children and young people. Together we have presented the training, Brainspotting with Children and Adolescents, several times, which was approved by Dr. Grand. We always enjoy the co-teaching as much as the training.

When Dr. Jacobi visited me in Vienna, we sat at my kitchen table, talking for hours about the content and structure of this book. She wrote an excellent description of what Brainspotting is in the introduction. It is an excellent overview of Brainspotting and worth reading even if you are already a very experienced Brainspotting professional.

My gratitude goes out to her for her courage and wisdom during Brainspotting treatments with
children, families, and communities as for all her input and ongoing support in spreading the word about Brainspotting.

My very special thanks go to **Dr. David Grand** for his wisdom in his discovery of Brainspotting and his perseverance and courage to spread and develop his discovery. He always trusted and encouraged me in my Brainspotting work with children, which gave me the confidence and motivation to write this book.

My heartfelt appreciation goes to **"Hermana Maria,"** an Italian nun living in Paraguay. She was "Mom" to 50 children and young mothers in a children's home in Paraguay. She gave me access to a world that I could not have otherwise experienced. Through her trust, I was able to meet numerous children whose life stories were unknown, and it was apparent how much Brainspotting helped these children. The principle of uncertainty was reaffirmed daily. Her open arms toward the children and her open arms toward me made much of the content of this book possible.

My personal gratitude also goes to **Dr. Montserrat Armele**. She is an outstanding and well-known neuropsychologist in Paraguay and throughout South America. She shares her knowledge and experience by teaching many other psychologists so that they can also become well trained in children's neuropsychology. She trusted my Brainspotting treatments and was curious to learn more about it. Teamwork with her was enriching and provided me with knowledge of South American methods of treatments. Due to her professionalism, combined with a warm and supporting heart, I learned a lot from her and won a very special friend.

I also want to thank all my psychological companions during my professional development. My friend, **Mag. Karin Welsch**, whom I literally met during my first hour of studying psychology, and who has stuck by me through thick and thin. **Prof. Jerilynn Radcliffe** supported me in the Children's Hospital of Philadelphia during a three-month scholarship program. She gave me broad insight into the world of children's psychology in the inpatient unit and in the outpatient settings, always encouraging me to dive into the American culture. **Dr. Renate Fuiko** was my Austrian psychological role model. She continues to work at the Viennese University Children's Hospital, and through her guidance, I learned to combine psychological flexibility and professionalism during several years spent in the brain tumor unit. I have continued a deep friendship with all of my professional colleagues, never forgetting what I could learn from them.

I would also like to thank **Serene Calkins** who was reading this book with positive critical eyes. She provided me with her wisdom and enthusiasm about Brainspotting while helping with one or another English expression.

To complete my notes of appreciation, I would like to mention **all the children and adolescents, their families, and caregivers** who taught me and still teach me by being pure and authentic. They have shown me how well Brainspotting can be applied to children, and the depth of healing that can take place for the younger age group. Their trust allows me to continue learning from case to case and enjoy it in a way that makes me eager to share it with the reader.

Foreword by Dr. Martha S. Jacobi

When I answered David Grand's telephone call in early October of 2014, little did I know that saying "yes" to his request to open my home to a Brainspotting Trainer-in-Training for the weekend would change my life and contribute to bringing an accessibility of Brainspotting to children around the world. Monika Baumann was traveling on less than a couple of days' notice to New York from Paraguay, her husband's home country, to learn how to teach Brainspotting to others. For two days, my colleagues and I sat in David's office in Manhattan talking Brainspotting for hours. Moni and I continued those conversations on our subway rides in and out of Queens, over coffee, breakfasts and dinners, and late into the evenings. We discovered parallel paths in our professional lives and developed a deep friendship as well as a collegiality such that, today, we do not always remember whose ideas came from whom. Since then, we have taught together, in person or online, in Brazil, Paraguay, Austria, the Netherlands, and the United States, and have co-authored several articles and chapters about Brainspotting with kids and adolescents. We have provided consultation and tutorials on using Brainspotting with kids to clinicians around the world, as internet-based video calls have become accessible, at least somewhat reliable, and affordable even in areas previously considered too remote to reach.

In the pages of this book, however, you will read of our journey through Monika's eyes and from her wide practice that spans two continents, three languages, and over two decades of dedicated work with children. You will also learn how Monika has furthered the work into applications with child-parts and ego-states of adults, developing several Brainspotting set ups that can be used effectively with clients across the age spectrum, and regardless of developmental age and stage. From her private practice in Vienna, Austria to her volunteer work with homeless and orphaned children in Paraguay, this book will detail the transformative power of Brainspotting in bringing healing to the most deeply wounded of young lives. Plentiful case vignettes illustrate the neuroscientific and developmental theories that support the extension of Brainspotting practice from the adolescent skater in whose therapy session David Grand discovered Brainspotting, to the youngest of children, even infants.

Monika Baumann brings to this book a wealth of knowledge and expertise in working with traumatized children and their families. Supplementing her training as a systemic neuropsychologist at the University of Vienna, she won a scholarship for a three-month practicum study under the supervision of Dr. Jerilynn Radcliff at the Children's Hospital of Philadelphia (Pennsylvania, USA). She also studied at the Lehranstalt für Systemische Familientherapie (Academy for Systemic Family Therapy) in Vienna. From that urban/suburban experience, Monika went on to gain "on the ground" exposure and experience to the sometimes rough conditions, as well as the heart and body attunement of kids and families in Paraguay, while also maintaining her practice in Vienna.

The CrocoDuck VariPets® developed out of Monika's cultural awareness of metaphors and animal species that could be relevant across multiple continents and her giftedness in storytelling and use of projective therapeutic strategies in working with kids. I would be remiss in not mentioning the love and support of Monika's husband Luis, and daughters, Carolina, Claudia, and Cristina, who have been there every step of the way, and have also opened their homes to me. Brainspotting with kids is an inspirational family matter in the Baumann household. They helped bring the VariPets® into a reality that is now supporting the training of Brainspotting therapists around the world in learning to use Brainspotting with children, with particular emphasis given to clinicians working in developing countries and/or poverty-laden conditions.

The case vignettes and commentary of this book will delight, encourage, and challenge Brainspotting practitioners and all who work and live with kids, into new ways of helping them recover from the wounds that life brings their way. Enjoy the read; savor the healing. Inspiration for expanding your practice with creativity and joy "sits and waits" in the pages of this book.

Thank you, Monika, for the journey thus far together! Following the tails of our littlest comets, who knows where the future will lead...

Martha S Jacobi, New York City, November, 2020

About The Author

Monika Baumann is a clinical neuropsychologist and family therapist in Vienna. She regularly spends time in her husband's homeland of Paraguay, where she helped for years in a group home of more than 50 abandoned children ranging in age from 0 to 18. While in Paraguay, she voluntarily "Brainspots" frequently in a school in the countryside and is involved in other social projects. She and her husband have three young adult daughters, all of whom support her in her Brainspotting work.

Monika Baumann is a contracted Brainspotting trainer with Brainspotting Trainings LLC (BTL).

Together with Dr. Martha Jacobi, a wonderful Brainspotting trainer in New York, a specialized training program, "Brainspotting for Children and Adolescents," was developed and approved by BTL. Recently this was extended to a three-day training and is offered around the world.

How it all began ...

Several years ago, I was with my family in the countryside of Paraguay doing volunteer work in a school. A friend and therapist from Vienna came to visit me, and I told her that I was concerned about two schoolchildren. She suggested that Brainspotting would be the best treatment for them.

I asked myself if a treatment with a stick, as she explained it to me, could be something serious, or would it be one of those alternative "upcoming and quickly gone" techniques? Several hours later, I found myself researching Brainspotting. Having already done a lot of trauma work with kids as well as adults the "eye-brain-body connection" sounded serious to me, and I became curious.

Some weeks later, I found myself in the first training with Dr. David Grand asking him if Brainspotting would also work with kids and adolescents. He gave me an encouraging smile and responded that he would love for me to go out, try it and let him know!

This is exactly what I did, and I became confident in Brainspotting and its great effects – with adults as well as children of all ages.

The book's story

In this book, I attempt to model how Brainspotting with kids and adolescents could be done from the first contact to the last moment of being with them and in their social surroundings. Therefore, reading this book can be compared with a session from the beginning to the end, remembering that flexibility is the keyword for "trusting the process."

I used a lot of practical examples from my experience to explain the theory. To maintain data protection and to keep "children's' lives safe," all case descriptions have been changed in a way that the persons behind them cannot be identified.

Although there is a lot of information and experience given in the following pages, the aim is that you forget all about it while doing Brainspotting with young clients, and be yourself: trusting, observing, and experiencing how much is going on in those developing brains!

CHAPTER 1

INTRODUCTION TO BRAINSPOTTING AND HOW TO LEARN IT

WHAT IS BRAINSPOTTING?

If you are reading this book, you may already be familiar with Brainspotting. Maybe you heard about it from a friend, family member, or colleague. Maybe you have received Brainspotting therapy. Possibly you are already a trained Brainspotting therapist, consultant, or a trainer colleague. Perhaps you picked it up because it is about helping hurting children feel better. Regardless, it follows Brainspotting's "no assumptions!" model.

The following 3 short "life Introductions" will give you a brief insight about how Brainspotting can appear in different age groups. In all three you will find the basics of connecting symptoms with body feelings and a Brainspot in the visual field.

Finally, my friend and great Brainspotting Trainer Dr. Martha Jacobi from New York, gives us an "adult insight," which is an excellent help to understand what I will talk about in the rest of the book.

"Where you look affects how you feel..."

A two and a half-year-old
Professional: Oh, poor little Ann. Can't sleep at night?
Ann: Looks to the floor, nodding her head.
Professional: You know what, I can remember that I also wanted to go to my parents' bed when I was little.
Ann: Looks up to me with big eyes and puts her thumb in her mouth.

Professional: See who I have here? May I introduce Benny the sleep bear to you?

Ann: Nods yes with a soft smile.

Professional: Benny always is so afraid at night. He lies in his bed and turns around and around but can't sleep.

Ann Doubtful: Really?

Professional Yes. Do you have an idea where his bed is in here? I want you to help him.

Ann: Points to my right. Sucking her thumb even harder.

Professional:Here?

Ann: Hmm.

Professional: Good - here? Together we can prepare a "bed" for the bear.

Can you help me cure the bear of his sleeplessness?

Ann: Happy nodding.

ProfessionalWhere in his body does Benny feel his "turning around" when he wants to sleep?

Ann: Points to the head

Professional: Ah.

Ann: Softly starts touching the bear on his head while looking at him.

She takes the thumb out of her mouth and I can engage her in role-play in which the bear gets cured while she expresses with her body language and a few words what Benny is feeling physiologically and emotionally.

A 7-year-old child comes to my office and asks:

Child: Can you really take away my nightmares and rage attacks?

Professional: Sorry my dear, I definitely can't do that.

Child: But my father told me you can.

Professional: Well, let me tell you and your dad that I would not like to, even if I could. What would happen if you could not defend yourself anymore and you would come into a difficult situation? What would happen if your brain would not be alert anymore?

Child: Aha! So it is not bad that I am aggressive? But I do not like my nightmares!

Professional: Look, I would like to explain to you that neither your nightmares nor your being like a volcano is necessary right now. But they are good to have, in case you need them. What I would like to try to achieve with you and your dad and your eyes is that you do not need to have rage attacks and nightmares when life is good and safe.

Child: You need my eyes?

Professional: Sort of. Your eyes are so close to your brain. By integrating them as helpers, we might get your brain to feel the difference between being safe and being in danger.

Child: Wait, wait, wait! My eyes are here – what do they need to do?

Professional: Well, let's think about the feelings you have when you are aggressive or have nightmares.

Child: I hate myself. I get hot and then I explode, and at night I tremble.

Professional: So, if you tell me that now, can you just look at this little bear (finger-puppet) on my pointer. The bear feels exactly like you. Let's see where he feels it the most.

I pull the bear on the pointer from my left side to my right side.

Child: Uh oh. Here I am getting that volcano feeling – my stomach gets mad.

Professional: You know what? I think this is the place where your eyes should look now to help you with these feelings. Let's see what is happening.

A 13-year-old:

Adolescent: ...and during the test, I can't remember what I learned before and what I knew perfectly yesterday. I am sitting there completely blocked, trembling and full of panic.

Professional: Telling me that I realize that you are highly desperate in these moments and your body even trembles.

Adolescent: Yes, and there is no way to come out of that.

Professional: Well, let us see. I have learned a special technique called Brainspotting. It might be of great use, as this treatment tries to stimulate your self-healing capacities for both body feelings and emotions.

Adolescent: Aha - What do I have to do for that?

Professional: Well, it might sound different. I use a pointer and need you to look at it. I'll show you. What do you feel now, as we talk about your block?

Adolescent: Somehow bizarre – I hate talking about it, I am so ashamed because I never was like that. It makes me feel helpless, I just hate it.

Professional: Can you let me know where in your body you feel that helplessness?

Adolescent: Well – that's weird, but I think it sits in my chest. I am getting really hot from there.

Professional: Okay, and if you now look at this pointer, where do you feel it the most? If I hold the pointer to your right, or to your middle or to your left? (I demonstrate this with the pointer.)

Adolescent: To my right, over there it is really hot.

Professional: Good, let me see exactly where...

After having found the Brainspot, a great integration process could take place.

In all three descriptions, you see how Brainspotting can spontaneously be applied. Although these dialogues seem like simple professional situations, Brainspotting is truly integrated.

Dr. Martha Jacobi gives us an "adult" explanation of what Brainspotting is to make those intuitive examples from above understandable in the sense of Brainspotting.

Description from Dr. Martha Jacobi:

This is a book about a brain-body approach to healing and wholeness that is called Brainspotting, and how it can be used with kids and adolescents.

Brainspotting is an approach to healing and wellness that is deeply rooted in the body's nervous system. It appears to activate the brain's innate self-scanning and self-healing capacities in the context of a neurobiologically and relationally attuned interpersonal encounter. In Brainspotting, a person's brain-body activation around a particular issue is paired with a relevant eye and orienting position, called a Brainspot. Brainspots access neurophysiological systems that hold emotional and/or physical experience in an often wordless but "felt" form of memory. The Brainspot opens these memory "files" (neurophysiological systems) in the context of a highly attuned clinical and neurobiological relationship, allowing the brain-body system as a whole and the relevant neurophysiological systems to re-regulate and re-orient to the present in an adaptive manner. When this happens, the prior activation eases; the person feels—and functions—better (Grand, 2003-1017; Jacobi).

Brainspotting was discovered in 2003 by Dr. David Grand, a psychotherapist from Long Island, New York, in the middle of a therapy session with an adolescent, elite competitive ice skater. Grand (who says he prefers to be called "David" by clients and trainees alike), was already a highly skilled and successful therapist and international training instructor at the time. He had worked with 16-year-old "Karen" for more than a year, trying to help her overcome a problem with what she said should be a simple jump in her skating: the triple loop jump. When Karen attempted the jump, she said that she would feel her legs go "numb" and forget her program. Karen had processed many traumas directly related to her skating, as well as family concerns that had negative consequences for her. Overall, she felt better, and was skating well, except for that one jump. Her inability to complete it successfully in a competition held her back from achieving her hopes, dreams, and skating goals.

On one particular day, David was using a variation of a mind-body therapy that involved having Karen make slow, steady eye movements, following or "tracking" David's fingers moving back and forth horizontally at Karen's eye-level. All of a sudden, something different happened. Instead of tracking smoothly, Karen's eyes froze on a spot and wobbled there. David says he felt his own hand and arm "lock" onto that spot as well. His hand and her eyes, stopped and stayed on that spot for the next ten minutes or so. During that time, Karen processed what seemed like a torrential flow of memories, body sensations, and emotions. She took a deep breath, and as David reports it, both of them wondered, "What just happened?" All they knew at the time was that in that ten-minute period, Karen not only processed previously unaddressed issues, but also processed to new depths, issues that both of them thought she had already worked through and resolved.

Early the next morning, Karen went to the skating rink to practice. When she attempted the triple loop, she landed on the ice again, but to her surprise, she landed solidly and cleanly on her blades with all the mid-air turns perfectly completed! Then she did it again. And again. And again. Over and over she did it until, back in his office, David received an excited call from Karen. "David! I did it! And I did it again, and again, and again."

What was different about that session? What happened when Karen and David both stopped instinctively on that fixed, apparently relevant, eye position?

David began to watch for similar eye responses in his other clients. He told his consultee therapists about what happened and encouraged them to "watch for this" with their clients. Over the next several months, reports started coming in from around the world. Clients were healing more deeply and more thoroughly with the fixed eye position than they had previously done.

The quest to identify and understand the relational and

neurobiological processes of those ten minutes that changed Karen's skating and her life, has continued progressively and relentlessly since then. So also, has the quest to present a clear, simple, and specific scientific theory of Brainspotting, accompanied by evermore nuanced forms of Brainspotting techniques.

At the time of this writing, there are about 80 Brainspotting trainers spread across six continents, and more than 14,000 trained Brainspotting therapists in the world. A body of scientific research confirming the ongoing clinical results is growing steadily around the world (Grand, 2013), (Corrigan, 2015) (Hildebrand, 2014, 2017), (Anderegg), (Grand, 2011).

A community self-study from Sandy Hook in Newtown, CT shows that Brainspotting is reported as the most effective healing modality there for adults and is perceived by the community to be one of the four most effective healing modalities for the children and youth below the age of 18 (Distribution Committee of the Sandy Hook School Support, 2016).

HOW DOES IT WORK?

Brainspotting embraces a principle of "uncertainty" in interpersonal encounters by acknowledging the vast terrain hidden in the depths of the human brain. Neuroscientists report that there are over one quadrillion connections in the human brain, which is more than the number of known stars in the universe! Every brain, therefore, is unique.

Brainspotting therapists work very much in the here and now with whatever their clients bring up in sessions, and seek to help their clients access the deepest, subcortical parts of their brain-body systems. They do this by pairing their clients' awareness of brain-body activations with a relevant eye and orienting position, called a Brainspot. Clients can then hold their gaze on the Brainspot position during the session, in the service of healing.

Brainspots are identified through one or both eyes. In Brainspotting trainings, we teach students to locate Brainspots from an "outside window" observation of the client's reflexive responses (i.e., blink, eye twitches or wobbles, pupil dilation, quick breaths and subtle body shifts); "inside window" reporting by the client of her/his "felt sense" (Gendlin, 1976); or Gazespotting, "a naturally occurring fixed and relevant eye position" (Grand, 2013).

Brainspotting, is thus "a powerful, focused treatment method that works by identifying, processing and releasing core neurophysiological sources of emotional/body pain, trauma, dissociation and a variety of challenging symptoms. Brainspotting is a simultaneous form of diagnosis and treatment..." [It is] "deep, direct, powerful yet focused and containing... [and] adaptable to almost all areas of specialization" (Grand, 2013).

I want to invite you to try the following exercise:

1. Think of something that bothers you a bit.
2. Become aware of how your body feels. Where in your body do you feel activated?
3. Rate your level of "bothered" activation in your body,

on a scale from 0 to 10, where 10 is high, and 0 is neutral.

4. Look a little to your left for a while, and see how you feel.

5. Next, look straight ahead for some time, and see how you feel.

6. Then look to your right, and see how you feel.

7. Compare how you feel in these three directions. Was one stronger than the others? Did you feel relief in one area but not in the others?

8. Just notice...where you look can make a difference in how you feel.

That's how Brainspotting works.

WHAT ACTUALLY HAPPENS IN A BRAINSPOTTING SESSION?

In a Brainspotting session, like any other therapy session, a client comes in because something in her/his life isn't working the way the client wants it to. The therapist and the client talk about what is happening for the client in the present, and what the client's relevant life history has been. What is different about a Brainspotting session, at this point, is that the therapist is mindful of what might be happening in the client's brain in relation to the reason why the client is coming for treatment. The therapist is also taking notice of any spontaneously occurring Brainspot that the client uses when talking about her/his problems or symptoms.

As the therapist develops an empathic and attuned relationship with the client, the therapist also talks with the client, in an age, cultural, and life-situation appropriate manner, about the brain and how it works, as well as what happens when a person gets "stuck" with the thoughts, feelings, and behaviors that are called "symptoms." Optimally, in the first session, a Brainspotting therapist will also talk with the client about Brainspotting and how it works.

The client may listen to music or nature sounds on a CD/MP3 track that has been specially recorded ("BioLateral Sound" by David Grand or one of several other available recordings) to move the sound in interweaving waves between the right and left ears. The bilateral sound effect is understood to help the client's brain integrate processing between its right and left hemispheres, and for most people, to provide gentle containment for processing.

Once the client is clear about what she/he wants to work on, the therapist asks the client to think about that issue and allow the brain-body activation related to it to become present. The client is then asked to rate the strength or intensity of the activation on a scale from 0 to 10, where 0 is neutral and 10 is the most activated that the client can imagine. When the client has identified the location of the activation in her/his brain-body system, a Brainspot relevant to the activation is located as a means of accessing the neurological functioning that is keeping the client feeling stuck. The Brainspot is located with an outside window (OW), inside window (IW), or Gazespotting (GSP) approach, as described above. The client is then invited to hold a gaze on the Brainspot, to "go inside" and with mindful focus, to observe her/his own internal process.

The therapist checks in with the client periodically from there on, but as little as possible in order not to interfere with the client's process. Many Brainspotting sessions appear to be very quiet, in that neither the client nor the therapist speaks very much. However, in that verbal silence, the client is processing deeply.

In this way, with the therapist holding a frame that is grounded in the mystery and unknowable uncertainty of the client's process, coupled with deep relational and neurobiological attunement, and matched with the client's activation paired with a relevant internal eye and orienting position and an external fixed-gaze point, the client's brain-body system is given the opportunity to re-regulate, re-organize, and heal itself.

HOW TO LEARN BRAINSPOTTING?

Currently, the best way to start to learn Brainspotting is by attending a three-day training, Brainspotting Phase 1, through Brainspotting Trainings (BTL). After Phase 1 is completed, several advanced and specialty trainings are available as well. Reading the book *Brainspotting: The Revolutionary New Therapy for Rapid and Effective Change* (Grand, 2013) is highly recommended in addition to the trainings. Individual consultation with a Brainspotting expert or trainer approved by BTL is also recommended. Updated information about trainings worldwide and in your country as well as updates to the certification process can be found at www.brainspotting.com.

CAN BRAINSPOTTING BE USED WITH CHILDREN?

This question is often asked in Phase 1 trainings. Do you remember how old that competitive ice skater was when Brainspotting was discovered in her session? She was an adolescent. In fact, she was just 16 years old!

Since the time of Anna Freud (1895 - 1982), psychotherapy has been available for children, with adaptations made to match their developmental ages and stages. After Brainspotting was discovered, many of the clients were kids. Not only was Brainspotting effective with them, the children became co-creative collaborators in setting up their own therapeutic frames. Since then, many other therapists around the world, who already worked with kids, have been trained in Brainspotting. As experiences were shared, a commonality of conceptualization and how to use Brainspotting with kids was discovered, regardless of location or the language spoken by the clients. This book is an effort to share with you what was learned and experienced with this much-appreciated age group. (End of Dr. Jacobis introduction to Brainspotting)

WITH WHOM AND WHICH SYMPTOMS CAN BRAINSPOTTING BE APPLIED?

After Dr. Jacobi above gave us her wise insight into Brainspotting, I'd like to point out that this it is much more than a technique for traumatized persons. It is known to help integrate post-traumatic symptoms in a way that they do not "burden" us anymore.

The Greek translation of trauma is: "A psychological, emotional or mental trauma or psych trauma (τραύμα) referred to as an emotional injury". The word "trauma" comes from the Greek and generally means "wound" without specifying what caused it.

I personally experienced Brainspotting to be applicable to all effects of emotional and physical injuries. These include symptoms, behavioral issues, post-traumatic states, crisis, and psychosomatic issues.

Once the power behind it is experienced, it is hard not to use it.

AN ATTEMPT TO PRESENT BSP VISUALLY

One day I opened my mailbox and found a card showing a house being pulled out of deep water by some balloons. On the other side, some words explained the gratitude of a family who recently finished Brainspotting treatment. "We feel like the house on this card, being rescued at the last moment."

I placed that picture on my desk, enjoying thinking back to a deep and successful treatment period. A little later, I was asked to give a speech about Brainspotting. This card inspired me to visualize how Brainspotting could be explained. I made the following picture (Figure 1), which expresses one way that Brainspotting can be seen in a very simple way.

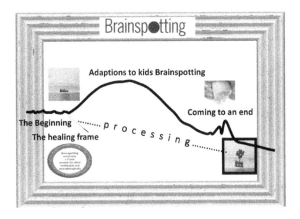

Figure 1: Brainspotting process visualization
Baumann

We meet children and adolescents in our working areas because of some reasons. Typically, something in their life is not going smoothly. We start to uncover the issues, symptoms or activation of our clients represented in this picture by the sinking house. Doing so, we create a relationship full of trust and presence. To set the relational and neurobiological frame is basic to whatever will come up during the integration process as something they could not work out yet. The frame gives stability. A Brainspot is found to connect the body feeling around the issue with a visual point. With the younger population, the Pointer is often replaced by stuffed animals, finger puppets, Post-Its to draw on or any other creative tool. The Brainspot is found through observation (Outside Window), together with the client (Inside Window) or as a Gaze spot. From there, the professional follows the young ones in the sense of uncertainty like the tail of a comet follows its head. We constantly take care of the brain-body connection and ask for body feelings. While our clients look at the Brainspot, they process post traumatic experiences, emotional wounds, side effects from injuries, etc. In this picture, this is represented by the wave, which could have many different forms. With children processing can be done as co-creative storytelling, imagination, drawing, listening to them, etc. Frequently it is supported with biolateral sound. We as therapists are often surprised how much is happening without needing to intervene, but rather, being present and waiting to see what will come. Brainspotting uses the phrase "Squeezing the lemon" to verify how much of the issue is still there after processing. This can be done by asking questions, observing, finding out about body feelings etc. If suitable an emotional process can be restarted. Finally, "the house is rescued" and we take care to see how this feeling can be integrated in the future life of the client.

Figure 1 is an attempt to visualize a Brainspotting session and will repeatedly help throughout the book to orientate where we are concerning the Brainspotting treatments.

This first part: "From the Very Beginning Onward" allows you to experience an unfolding parallel process of how Brainspotting can be used with the younger population. "The Beginning!" presents core relational elements of the first stages of Brainspotting sessions with kids. "The Healing Frame" discusses Brainspotting's "dual attunement frame"—the relational as well as the neurobiological—in the context of the interacting systems in which children live and relate.

"Adaptions for Brainspotting with Kids," provides an extensive, but by no means exhaustive, review of technical adaptations for helping children to process effectively in light of neurodevelopmental concerns. "Processing" will show how kids process their issues and what needs to be taken care of with them.

After learning how to finish Brainspotting treatments the second part, "Helpful Tools and Attitudes for Brainspotting Treatments with Children and Adolescents" explains uncertainty, creativity, parts work, and ways of setting.

The book ends with the chapter "Spreading Brainspotting Seeds," which is a short invitation to trust yourself in using this powerful technique.

CHAPTER 2

FROM THE VERY BEGINNING ONWARD

2.1. The beginning

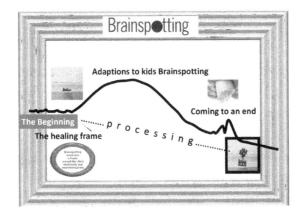

Figure 2: Brainspotting process visualization (Beginning)
Baumann

HOW IT STARTS.....

As I opened the door of a children's home in Paraguay, a little girl about five years old, ran across the pathway toward me and jumped up to greet me. I picked her up and hugged her. She looked at me and asked, "Can you treat me today; please can you treat me today?" Holding her, I glanced at her face and asked, "Now? Immediately?" A few moments later, I found myself with her on the floor, holding a blade of grass as my pointer and talking about profound feelings.

Brainspotting with the young ones does not start when we have the pointer in our hands. It starts when we come into contact with the child or adolescent, the family, or the caregivers. Once we arrange the first meeting, doubts and fears concerning the Brainspotting process are removed. Our way of listening, talking, and asking facilitates a trustful therapeutic relationship that is appropriate for the treatment of emotionally hurt children.

Wherever we conduct the treatment, the first contact with the affected child is extremely valuable. One way of expressing being with them is to meet them at eye level. Moving down to their height or lifting them up (if the culture allows), looking into their faces, and expressing that we like being with them although something in their life does not work, deepens the relationship! The challenge is to spark the child's curiosity about us and about the healing process. Being authentic or being ourselves as therapists strengthens the connection between young ones and adults.

Listening to young clients or their caregivers who brought them and determining what their issues are opens the doors to Brainspotting. All reactions that kids show are important and justified responses. Our brains are very smart! They don't just agree to be good, obedient, compliant, etc. Our brains also know from the beginning that they can defend or protect themselves, maybe by being aggressive, maybe by being shy, and so forth. Explaining this is a way of saying, "However you react is a good and valuable reaction. It might not be in balance with the rest of your reaction possibilities...so let's help your brain come away from this unbalanced way of behaving."

Most young people with trauma symptoms have never heard that their way of being is understandable until they meet with a trauma therapist who does not try to change them, but helps them to acknowledge, accept, and even respect and like their post-traumatic symptoms.

Going back to the practical example from the little girl in the children's home at the beginning of this chapter, one might argue that Brainspotting began too quickly with the young girl. However, she had already observed the treatment and its outcomes with other kids, and she was ready to be treated. There was no need for any explanation or preparation, as she felt the deep wish to be treated. Holding her in my arms and observing her made it clear to me that it was important to "do it now."

This example demonstrates that while there are facts, knowledge of theory and techniques, behaviors, and positions a trauma therapist should have, sometimes – and this is the essence of good treatment – it is just as important to grab the opportunity of the moment, with all of its uncertainties, and pregnant possibilities!

"HOW TO DISSOLVE TRAUMA SYMPTOMS WITH CHILDREN AND ADOLESCENTS" - SOME EXPLANATION MODELS

The following two completely different case examples demonstrate different explanation possibilities:

A 10-year-old boy and his parents sat in my private practice, hoping to rid the boy of his anxiety symptoms. The family wanted to know how I would help this boy. I took out my brain model and explained to them what happens in the brain during a traumatic situation, as well as what happens in the brain during the Brainspotting process, using a description the 10-year-old could understand. After that, I switched to the treatment process, to determine if they were fine with Brainspotting and explained what the long-term results of success could be.

In my first therapeutic meeting with 7-year-old Maria and her parents, they told me that she was blocked in mathematics. This happened not only when she had to say something in front of her classmates, but also when she did her homework. The parents said that from the moment she had to do mathematics, she became unhappy, angry and disappointed. I listened to them and spontaneously took out a stuffed animal. I told the little girl, that this "pet" had exactly the same problem and asked her where it should sit, to let us know how it felt to have to do mathematics. Maria pointed to my left. I moved my chair to the access point and put the animal on my knee and we started talking about how the pet felt and what it hated about mathematics. Maria knew exactly... and in this way, we started a Brainspotting process in the first ten minutes of meeting each other.

These diverse explanations attempt to express that it is often useful and even necessary to explain our way of working and especially what Brainspotting is. A different way of beginning Brainspotting is to just start when the kids are already activated, and the situation is ready for it. An explanation in such situations can prohibit the process. This happens when the emotional strain of a client is high, and the clients urgently want to get rid of their symptoms. It is up to us as therapists to assess if the situation is "safe" and, when it is, nothing should stand in the way of active processing with a Brainspot.

SOME PROPOSALS FOR EXPLAINING
BRAINSPOTTING TO YOUNG PEOPLE

The brain-related description

Talking about the brain is complicated. It is such a complex organ it seems indescribable. The use of a tool to make it more visible or tactile can be of great help. A multi-part model of the brain that can be taken apart is an excellent teaching device. A simple sheet of paper and a pen are also effective helping tools. Smart phones can be helpful by offering "brain explanation apps." Where there are no tools or for a quick explanation, a hand can be used for explanation.

With the use of such aids, a "hypothetical brain explanation" can be used. I always emphasize that the following description is hypothetical, although many physicians and neurobiologists have confirmed it to be well thought out and a possible true explanation. The brain remains a great secret.

In our brains the limbic system sits right in the middle between the neocortex and the brainstem. I also like to call it the emotional brain and it can be compared to a library of feelings. Every book in it represents an emotion, such as happiness, sadness, anxiety, and self-protection. All emotions, both those that are liked and not liked, are there together. There is always activation, even while sleeping. Being relaxed or having nightmares means to feel. In every moment, feelings occur, i.e., when playing, studying, watching television, being in a conflict, helping in the kitchen, or replacing the car tires. At least one book in our limbic system feeling library is always activated.

Sometimes, when something sad or shocking happens, the limbic system (or feeling library) does not want this dangerous or threatening feeling to be allowed in there. It might make a huge mess, so the librarian believes it is better to forbid it to come in. An alarm or control system (the amygdala) goes off any time the feeling is near. What a difficult situation! There is a dangerous feeling in the brain that cannot go where it belongs, and it decides to find another place. The easiest way is for it to pass down! On its way, it bypasses the "survival center" where the reactions flee, fight, and freeze are based. From there, the body gets the information to react, for example, with pounding heartbeats, stomach aches, trembling, depression, anger, aggressiveness, fatigue, etc.

The librarian is quite happy that it worked well and continues to listen and react to the alarm. Symptoms that are somehow related to the flight, fight, and freeze reactions become chronic and are not only post-traumatic disorders, but they can also be simple behavior problems, somatic issues, etc.

At that point, I often describe eyes as "superheroes" because they have a special connection to the feeling and survival center. Therefore, they can help the librarian or the alarm center to see that the feeling is ok. To accomplish this, I might need the help of the child to tell the story of the problem, using her/his "superheroes" (eyes).

At this point, I typically step back from the conversation with the young client and ask with curiosity, "What would happen with the symptoms of aggressiveness, heartbeat pounding, stomachache, etc. after that?" Usually, the kids understand that the symptoms would not be felt at all or at the same strength anymore.

Storytelling

Before I first went to Paraguay, where people speak Spanish (my mother language is German), I looked for a symbolic story to explain Brainspotting to the younger ones. The following Grimm Brothers' fairy tale came to mind.

Once upon a time, there was a princess who was playing with her golden ball. All of a sudden it fell into a deep well and she wept bitterly. Unexpectedly an ugly frog emerged from the depths and offered to bring the ball back. His condition was that from now on she had to take him as a playmate everywhere and treat him lovingly. The princess promised everything and the frog returned her golden ball. Overjoyed, she ran home, disobeying her promise.

During the family dinner, the frog knocked on the door. The princess was frightened and told her father what had happened. He advised and supported her to be loving and respectful with the frog. Although it disgusted the princess enormously, she adhered to her father's advice. Being in her playroom with the frog, she accepted him. In some story versions, she kissed the ugly frog; in other versions, she threw him angrily against the wall.

Whatever she did, the ugly frog received attention, which enabled him to turn into the former prince he was and they lived happily ever after (Grimm, 1812).

I like to compare this familiar fairy tale to Brainspotting. The princess represents our clients and receives the support of her father, who represents the therapist. Through this support, she gains the courage to approach the unpleasant, even though her body feels the ugliness of the situation. She is able to face the trauma and her body feelings, which are associated with the ugly frog. Due to the different versions of the story (kiss or throw against the wall) we learn that trauma work can be emotionally stressful as well as very relieving. After confronting her reality, the "disgusting" frog becomes less disgusting by turning into a prince. The access point turns into a resource point and this makes her deeply happy.

This story creates curiosity about Brainspotting and its outcome. Another way to use the story during the Brainspotting process is to put a finger puppet (frog) on the pointer and after squeezing the lemon, the child is given the opportunity to exchange the finger puppet with another one (frog to the prince). In addition, painting an ugly frog on one side of a paper and then painting the prince on the other side, can be another way to use the story. In this case the drawing can replace the pointer.

Pictures from Mark Grixti´s book which is illustrated by Rosanna Dean:

Mark Grixti published the following book to explain Brainspotting, which can be purchased online: (Grixti, 2015)

The following three pictures (Figure 3), taken out of the book, help visualize Brainspotting in an imaginative way and allow for an easy explanation.

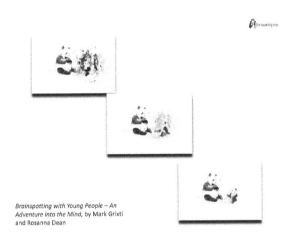

Brainspotting with Young People – An Adventure into the Mind, by Mark Grixti and Rosanna Dean

Figure 3: Brainspotting Illustration
Mark Grixti, Rosanna Dean

In the first picture of Figure 3, the little panda bear is full of his symptoms. The symptoms are seen chaotically and colorfully around his head so that the little panda bear is hardly seen.

In the second picture, when the young panda is looking at the bamboo and talking with the grown-up panda bear, his symptom becomes less important. They are still there, but the signs are clearing up!

Finally, in the third picture, the little panda bear sees what he really is. There are still some symptoms, but they are as important as anxiety is in protecting ourselves.

Engaging the child´s interest and curiosity in Brainspotting!

Maybe you remember when you were in school and received poor results on an assignment or test. Isn´t it the worst if one child is the only one among all the other kids to score poorly. It is less embarrassing when nearly all the others also have poor results.

Sharing common experiences of other kids (obviously no names or details) who had done Brainspotting with me and felt better after it, is a way of saying, "You are not the only one with this problem and there is a great way to help. Are you curious?" The moment the kid shows interest, you can explain Brainspotting in whatever way you choose, or move along the X-axis (horizontal) and let them feel their own body reactions.

The parking brake explanation

A simple form of explaining is to make a comparison with a car. You and your client in front of you are as great as your most desired auto brand. Imagine that this fabulous car is driving with the parking brake pulled. While it begins to smell of burnt rubber, the car continues to drive with the break on, without even remotely utilizing its potential. Life seems similar when we suffer post-traumatic stress disorder.

Releasing the parking brake is a good way to make a car function smoothly again. For a human being, Brainspotting is one of the great techniques, which can help us "function" again in the sense of using all the potential with which we are gifted.

Some proposals for integrating Brainspotting into a given situation without explaining Brainspotting (- it happens intuitively).

The explanations given above are often used. Still, it is important to recognize, accept, and understand that sometimes no explanation is necessary to achieve processing. Kids offer many possibilities to spontaneously begin Brainspotting. It is simply necessary to stay with the basics you have learned offering Brainspotting and adapting to the classical way of doing it in a given situation. As taught in all trainings, staying in the tail of the comet is one core piece.

In the following list, you find some ideas how you can integrate a Brainspotting Process spontaneously with children and adolescents.

- Start telling a story and let the child identify with the leading character. The kid may tell the emotional part of the story (co-creative storytelling)
- Offer the child to ask the magic wand. (E.g: If this pointer could tell us, how you feel....)
- Sit on the floor constructing something and make a part of the game a representative for the Brainspot. (E.g: Which of these blocks would stand for your anxiety?)
- Use a stuffed animal to replace the pointer.
- Indicate that you notice that the client is catching a gaze

spot on a spot over there. Ask: "What do you feel staring at it?"

- Use painting materials and let feelings be expressed by colors
- Ask: "If you could see all that on TV, where in this room would the screen be to see it in the best way?"
- Use the pointer as the target of the child's fantasy: Imagine your symptom would sit on the pointer. What does it look like? How do you feel seeing it?

What can be done, when children, families or systems refuse the Brainspotting treatment?

In most cases trust and a relational base allow good access to Brainspotting. Sometimes as professionals, we are confronted with individuals, families, or systems that absolutely refuse to do trauma work or to allow their system to integrate something they suffer from. It is important to get their commitment by trying to discover what causes them to refuse to "get help." Addressing this directly might be a way of motivating them. It has often been observed that refusing help can be a form of the brain trying to protect the person.

I remember an adolescent girl who came to my office because of sleeplessness and fear. I offered her Brainspotting and she devalued that idea. She was extremely defiant. Confronting her with her behavior in a very diplomatic way, she burst into tears and told me a secret of a friend being in danger due to drug abuse. We first had to find a way to deal with this situation and only then could we work out her anxieties and sleeping disorders with Brainspotting.

2.2. The healing frame

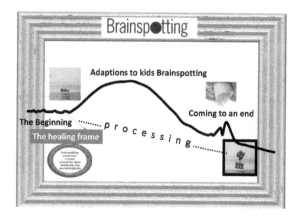

Figure 4: Brainspotting process visualization (Healing Frame)
Baumann

Framesetting provides the stability to allow a person to "process," which means to work out something they were not able to work out previously. This is similar to a painting when often the frame defines the best perspective for the artwork.

Brainspotting is a brain-body-based treatment. By adapting to our clients, we also observe and sense how they feel physiologically and emotionally in the given situation. The connection of those feelings and body sensations with the

Brainspot in the visual field allows processing, and in the long run, integration.

Brainspotting constructs a dual attunement frame around the client: relational and neurobiological. With each client, it is decided individually how tight or wide the frame is set. This leads to access through either resources or activation or a mixture of both. The aim is to provide the best possible processing in the given situation. Therefore, the frame can always be adapted to the process of each individual at any time in treatment.

We often confront situations representing the issue, such as the sinking house. The picture clearly expresses the hopelessness of kids in difficult situations. However, they react to a traumatic situation, they cannot envision "coming out of the water." Finding the Brainspot helps the young ones to go for an inner process and to express what they feel: either through their body language, words, or any other creative techniques. Integrating their emotional wounds during processing is always accompanied by the presence of a professional. In Figure 4 it is seen like a wave rising high and then trailing off. After processing and squeezing the lemon, the house could find a way in the direction of healing – again typical for kids: a simple, clear solution in which they believe.

Imagining the whole treatment as waves, it is important to recognize that some days they are rougher, more intense, coming quicker or slower or more silently than on other days. The Brainspotting processes are individual. We never know, but staying uncertain and allowing whatever comes by holding the frame is the trustful attitude and, therefore, a resource in itself that we can endow on our clients.

In Brainspotting we refer to the "dual attunement frame." This means not only being in a highly effective emotional relation with our clients, but also supporting their neurobiology during a Brainspotting treatment.

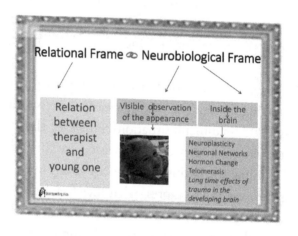

Figure 5: PowerPoint of the three-day "Brainspotting for Kids and Adolescents" training, 2019
Baumann

As presented here, the relational frame and the neurobiological frame are like a "loving couple." Each one accomplishes the other one to promote each other's potential. Taking both in account during treatment provides a maximum of attunement.

THE NEUROBIOLOGICAL FRAME

Offering Brainspotting

As seen in Figure 5, neurobiology can be seen as the visible **outside appearance** and what is happening **inside the brain** of a young person. How does this appear? What does their body language say when we meet them in the working places? (Levine, 2007) (Siegel, 2010) (Bryson, 2011). The outside appearance, the way children and adolescents say hello, combined with our gut feeling, gives us a "first impression" (not necessarily diagnosis) about their development and the state of their emotions.

I opened the door and a young, tall and thin adolescent was waiting to come in. Looking up to him I offered my hand and said "Hello." The boy answered with the voice of a five-year-old: "Hello, do you have blocks in your office?" I could immediately tell that this client, for some reason, (delay, state of shock, etc.) was in a much younger developmental state. I could also feel that he was happy to be in my office.

Inside brain changes are not visible. It is an advantage, but not necessary, to know about them as long as we can trust the processes in our clients' brains. The following example of "emotional and neurobiological attunement" expresses the importance of the interchange of those two factors.

A little boy came into my office. He hid behind his mom, holding onto her skirt, and I could hardly see his face. I bent down and started a verbal and body communication with him. Verbally, I mentioned that I'd love to see him, while my body began a communication play switching my glance several times from the right to the left side and behind his mother's skirt. He slowly gained confidence and finally stayed on one side and started looking into my eyes, still evaluating the situation. I remained lowered and waited and reached out my hand. After a while of confidence-building play, he shook my hand and greeted me. His facial expression showed relief.

Situations like this sometimes take 30 seconds and sometimes longer. These are the perfect combinations of emotional and neurobiological attunement. Talking, greeting, smiling, and trusting him allowed for emotional access. Observing the boy as he hid behind his mother, not wanting to show his face, holding on to her skirt, etc. are neurobiological signs that can be seen from the outside, ultimately leading to our handshake.

Hypothesizing about the child's inner brain changes could elicit such thoughts as, *"In the beginning of the situation a system of auto-protection was active. This slowly changed into curiosity and courageousness."* Regardless of how many neurons were fighting together, how the cortisol level changed, how the amygdala supported that step, the child may have learned a way of balancing self-protection, and the ability to trust. Although I actually had no idea what was going on inside the brain, it was great to see the expression of relief on the child's face. **Do I need to know more in the moment of attunement?**

In Brainspotting, the emphasis is on the importance of "being" (attuned presence) with the young person. However, the neurobiological research, results, and the brain development knowledge can be of great help. All brain explanations I have heard about reassure what I was allowed to experience while being present in many Brainspotting processes with all ages.

In one instance, Dr. Grand stated, "Any intervention we use, we should use to allow deeper processing." This is a short, clear sentence, expressing what I have tried to describe. Independently of the age of my clients, I repeatedly go back to David's statement asking myself: "Is the time right for a question or intervention?" With kids, I allow myself to respect my "gut feelings" even more than with adults, using them as a positive indicator for the Brainspotting flow.

Some helpful brain knowledge

One way of using the brain knowledge to provide deeper processing is explaining that the symptoms are primarily a healthy reaction of our smart protector: the brain.

Pete's family was on vacation in a foreign country. Pete (9 years old) was present when a stranger at a bus station stole the bag from his caregiver. The caregiver ran after the thief and left Pete alone. Pete reacted by freezing - no words or movements for the next few minutes. Back home, Pete refused to use the school bus. He preferred walking to school and started to have sleep disorders. During the Brainspotting process, Pete felt and described freezing and started crying. I had the impression that the "ice melted" when he was processing deeply in a safe area.

After that session, Pete could take the bus again and return to his normal life rhythms. His sleeping disorder disappeared.

In the following session, Pete and his parents wanted to know how a single meeting changed Pete's behavior so drastically. I tried to explain what could have happened neuro-biologically to Pete's brain. This gained their trust in the treatment. I assumed that during the shock situation, Pete reacted with a freeze reflex coming up from his deep limbic system. He immediately protected himself during the period in which he was left alone at the bus station in a foreign country. The school bus might have reminded his brain of the danger he had experienced during his summer vacation. By walking to school, he would avoid that danger. Finally, not being able to sleep well and relax might have meant that his brain would remain alert. He could not trust any more that he was safe, so he felt subconsciously responsible and preferred taking care of himself rather than relaxing during sleep.

This assumption, explaining that the trauma reaction of being frozen could have continued without actual danger in the form of not taking the bus and developing alert states, can help our clients understand a situation. It can support the outcome of a Brainspotting process, where the brain starts developing self-healing capacities and provides "neocortical assurance" for the client. Explanations like that should always be done before or after processing, never interrupting the self-healing capacity during processing.

Recently I saw a teenager who had problems sleeping in places other than in his home. He tried hard with many sleepovers at friends' homes, but every time at night, he felt sick and had to vomit. This provided a good reason for him to go back home.

In working with this boy, I described the function of the vagus nerve, which is connected between our emotional feeling center and most of our organs. I told the boy about it before we started to step into the Brainspotting process. I asked him to imagine that powerful connection. During the Brainspotting session, he mentioned that he felt like he was feeling to vomit. He did not like that sensation and asked me if this was the vagus nerve. He experienced a very deep process and, in the end, mentioned the release. *"Finally, there is no more vagus - vomit – feeling."* For this teenage boy, the neo-cortical explanation allowed him to understand unacceptable body sensations during activation.

It might help our young clients or us to share brain knowledge before or after processing with the aim of delving deeper into the issue. However, *during* a Brainspotting process, it would destroy the attitude of being present, staying in the tail of the comet, and letting ourselves be surprised where it takes us.

The following insights into brain activation will provide initial ideas about what might go on in the brain. They are simply and hypothetically described to make you curious for more knowledge. Still, be aware that brain knowledge can be seen as a support to allow processing or strengthen the positive feeling after processing, but it can never replace a pure deep process.

The brain-body connection becomes more and more of a research object (Porges, 2017). Kids mostly know where their symptoms reside in their bodies. Just asking them, "Do you have an idea where in your body the anxiety, aggression, etc. sits?" will show you that most know instinctively. The very young ones still have no language; however, observing them allows us to see their body expressions in their face, and their reactions, such as grumbling, staring, etc.

"Flight, fight, and freeze" come from the deep limbic system often called the reptilian brain. These are individual and involuntary reactions, which protect us during an emotional and dangerous situation. Many symptoms of kids, especially behavioral difficulties, are based on these reactions. Highly aggressive kids are in a permanent state of defense, and sometimes not able to distinguish between safe and dangerous surroundings. Anxious children could be described as being in a long-lasting fleeing mode. This list of symptoms could be endlessly continued, bringing most back to the flight, fight, and freeze mode.

The cortisol level in the brain is one of the stress hormones and has the capacity to adapt lifelong. It allows the therapist to speculate about the enormous chance to gain brain changes during a Brainspotting process. Someone who is always under stress may suddenly be able to relax, because the "motor" has calmed down through treatment, giving the cortisol level an opportunity to rebalance. This may be a tiny step, which brings drastic changes in life. For example, this can mean the difference between not being able to sleep well because of stress and then being able to trust and sleep (Health, 2020).

The toxic stress response

In recent years, research concerning the influence of toxic stress on the development of a child and its lifelong influence has gained enormous attention (Shonkoff, 2019). The stress response system is an essential and excellent mechanism to react to acute stress. In such situations, it protects us, makes us aware of taking care, keeps us alert, and is an important and useful companion. It becomes harmful when the stress situation either continues for a long time or the system reacts with stress responses without the external stress factor. Today, science is concerned with huge influences of stress on emotional development, learning abilities, and physical health (Chapman, 2014).

Developmental windows and sensitive periods refer to periods during the growing process of a child in which special skills are learned. For example, learning to walk takes place during a critical window between 10 and 18 months. When a child does not learn something during the window of a critical period, it becomes more difficult to catch up later.

When I learned this, I felt that Brainspotting clients might have the capacity to reopen such a "critical window" period to emotionally catch up with something they were not able to learn earlier. The first research to address this was conducted by Hensch in 2012 in his book, Re-opening Windows: Manipulating Critical Periods for Brain Development.

Observing adolescents during the Brainspotting processes I could see a lot of regression. Situations where they speak like young children, need a stuffed animal to continue the process, or similar activities appear. We still do not know if activating a critical window period is possible, but we see the outcome of deep healing, when we allow our clients to be whatever age they choose during the process they need to go through.

Last but not least I would like to mention **Dr. Damir del Monte** (Monte, 2020). He provides deep brain knowledge in the context of psychotherapy. Watching his videos and listening to him allows a deep understanding in our field.

We are grateful for the research outcomes from neurobiologists, psychologists, and medical doctors, a few of whom have been mentioned. You can find more on the website www.brainspotting-kids.com.

For now, let's build the bridge to trusting the process.

Trust pure body feelings

As Brainspotting therapists, it is our power to **trust the brain-body connection and the neuroplasticity** of our clients' brains for self-healing. Stress factors are memorized and retained by children in their bodies in much the same way as the contents of documents are saved on a hard disk of a computer. The way of memorizing and reacting has an impact on the development of the brain, the immune system, the cardiovascular system, and the metabolic system.

The brain is described as having the capacity to change the structure of neuronal networks. A simple comparison can be made between neuronal networks and a handmade sweater. If there were a hole on the shoulder, everybody would see the hole, overlooking the artisanship of the pretty pullover. The user might try to cover the hole, ashamed of wearing such a sweater. If the user could open the pattern and knit this part with the same wool again, everyone would see the pretty sweater and the user would proudly show it. Our neuronal networks seem to be similar. Although we can never change the traumatic experience (use the same wool), life can be lived with a less dramatic feeling and maybe even make us more resilient (proud to wear a self-knitted pullover).

In a Brainspotting process, we ask our (young) clients where their symptom "sits" in their bodies (where is the hole in your sweater), and they often spontaneously show us a place like the stomach, the throat, the head, etc. Children have never heard about the brain-body connection, but instinctively can tell us about it. It is important to trust them and allow the process to move forward wherever it leads in the sense of uncertainty (and like that have them redo the knitted pattern).

One of my most touching Brainspotting processes, which I believe to be the answer to our body-brain relation and the integrative nervous system, happened with a 4-month-old baby in a children's home.

I was waiting in the babies' room. The staff was fetching one baby after another to get them ready for feeding. Finally, only one little girl, about 4 months old, was left. I felt sorry for her being alone and picked her up. I held her in my left arm and played with a small toy animal in the other. Working so much with Brainspotting – mostly with first aid interventions - in the children's home, I started to use the animal as a pointer and drew a line in her visual field from her left to her right. The girl was carefully and happily watching the toy pet. Suddenly she went into intensive extension with her whole body (tightened and bent back) and I became stressed. I thought to my-

self, "What you are doing here?" and quickly put the pet down. Then I thought, "Stop! You have already activated the girl," but then I wondered what would happen if I stayed on that point. So, I went back to the activation point with the pet, and the girl reacted again. She bent back for a few seconds and then suddenly relaxed until she started to smile at the little pet! We continued a wonderful play together until she was taken away for her meal!

A few days later, one of the caregivers told me that this little girl did not extend anymore before feeding time. I had no idea about her tightening issues when I picked her up that day. I continued observing this little girl and asked the caregivers about her extending. It never returned. Today, I know and I am allowed to feel during Brainspotting sessions that it is not important to know what it was; only to recognize that there was something. Trusting and staying attuned allows healing.

I believe and experience that knowledge about neurobiology is truly important and can help therapists, parents of adolescents, and others to understand the young clients (brain) better. This shows us how fascinating our brain and the knowledge surrounding us is. Still, observing and catching neurobiological signs like tears and smiles are great ways to live an attuned presence.

In the beginning of this chapter I mentioned the "visible body reactions" on the one hand, and the knowledge about neurobiological processes taking place inside the brain on the other hand. Setting the neurobiological frame during Brainspotting with our clients gives us the possibility to adapt the balance of those two to each of our clients. As you could witness in the above examples, in the "bus-station case," neurobiological knowledge was necessary to share with the family to gain their trust. In the baby case only trust into neurobiology was necessary to gain healing.

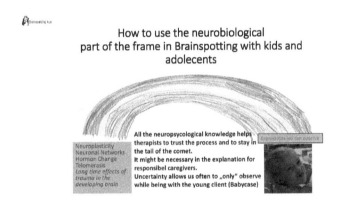

Figure 6: PowerPoint from the three-day "Brainspotting for Kids and Adolescents" training, 2019
Baumann

THE RELATIONAL FRAME

Another core piece of Brainspotting is providing the highest possible safety in our relationship with our clients. The relational attachment starts at the first contact and hopefully does not end during and beyond the therapeutic relatedness. With kids, it is helpful to express the relational attitude in direct and clear ways. We connect to the young ones with all our senses. Cultural aspects have an enormous importance.

Brainspotting begins long before we take out the pointer (or whatever we use instead to find the Brainspot).

Mom, Dad, one adolescent, and a tiny sister came to my workplace. A telephone call with the father in advance had made clear that the family should come together to treat the given issue with the adolescent boy. Opening the door, the young man stood beside his father. I reached out my hand and welcomed him. He shook my hand very weakly, demonstrating his insecurity. Immediately, I asked him if it was okay that I invited him with his family. He nodded his head positively. Still in front of him, I asked for his name and age and how they arrived. The little sister came between us. She was very active, and mentioned that he had been nasty to her on the way, and that his parents will think about an appropriate punishment for him when they return home. I bent down to her for a few seconds, explaining that I would get to her soon, but first I wanted to get to know her brother. I looked back at the boy, who seemed to be even more insecure. I moved my body up into a full standing position again in front of him. Giving him a silent smile, I mentioned that I could possibly help, and that he did not need to be punished and the little sister might be happy for her brother not to get a punishment. I then saw a glance of confidence in his eyes. I asked him who else he brought with him and he gently looked to his sister and responded, "my little beloved monster." I then bent down to her level and asked, "Now tell me who are these grown up people? Should we invite them to come in too? After shaking hands with the parents, they all come into my workplace.

Confidence starts in the first moment. Using all our senses in this very first moment helps to connect and opens a great field of opportunities. As you just read, I greeted the "issue client" first and bent down to the little girl. This is unusual in many cultures. Most professionals think that greeting the parents, caregivers, or responsible persons first is essential, as they are the ones who mostly initiated the sessions. They also love their child, and, in my experience, talking through the child to the parents makes them proud. It gives them the feeling that the professional takes charge of what it is going to be discussed. The young ones gain importance and trust in the therapist. Framesetting starts in these first connections.

Professionals get a "gut feeling" about developmental stage, character, current situation, etc. from the young ones in the first moments of meeting. This is an important puzzle piece for setting the dual attunement frame.

In another case, the relational connection allowed the neurobiological disorder to disappear before a Brainspotting process ever took place.

A family came to a social organization where I was offering treatments after they had been victims of an assault. I was prepared to welcome a father with his 8-year-old son and 5-year-old daughter. We decided that the mother should stay at home with her other kids, as they were not involved in the assault.

The three were experiencing post-traumatic disorders, such as sleeplessness, concentration difficulties, and increased aggressive behavior in the family. When they came to my workplace, I was shocked because no one had told me that the boy had a severe developmental delay. His walk was extremely stiff; he would not look at me; and he did not talk. As a therapist, I was a little disappointed, because I was not prepared for this situation. They all sat in my room and I started talking to the father and the little girl while I steadily observed the boy. He kept staring in a frozen manner and seemed not to understand what was going on.

At a certain point, I wanted to write down the family information. The boy started kicking his father strongly. I turned around to him and instinctively asked if there was a problem with his telling me the names. A horrified and demanding glance came back to me. I touched his shoulder and mentioned that I would just like to write down demographic dates, and that I was obliged not to tell anyone what we were going to talk about. The boy aggressively answered, "But they might find out our identity." To my surprise, he could talk normally. We started a conversation and I found out that the boy was extremely afraid that the offenders would find out their identity and return to their home and assault them there.

I put my sheet away, and promised the young boy that I would write down nothing and even "forget" their first names after the session. Suddenly his body became smooth, his voice clear and I soon discovered that he was an extremely bright, normally developed boy. Deep trauma work followed with the three of them. It would not have been possible, without setting this relational frame of trust and confidence.

Although I have chosen examples for either the relational or neurobiological frame, it is clear that one cannot exist without the other one.

In Brainspotting, we talk about framesetting when we decide which means of access to choose. Again, there is no recipe of whether to set the frame narrowly or widely. Often during the treatment, a narrow frame is widened or a loose large frame is tightened. Staying in the tail of the comet means to stay open for that move. This is as true for kids as it is for adults. We choose a narrow frame, including a resource spot, when we as professionals are not feeling safe to treat with high activation. Dr. Grand once stated the following: *"Firemen are going to the disaster and try to extinguish the fire. Depending on the strength of the fire (or disaster) they put on different protective clothing."*

I often think of this saying when choosing the appropriate frame. With adults, a conversation is possible, and together it can be decided which method of Brainspotting we use. The more they are lost in their being, the tighter the frame is set and, therefore, the more the resource model is chosen. Most of the time, resourcing is like an airbag – it is there if needed. Clients quickly understand that allowing a process and whatever is coming up during the processing is the resource, and integrating the traumatic issues aids the resource.

With kids, we are more like the captain of a boat. We also need the surroundings, such as family, school, kindergarten, etc. to be included in our decision, so we can choose which "protective clothing" is needed. Besides deciding how we set the frame, another dimension comes up before or during processing. Kids sometimes tell us that they are actually not protected and frequently exposed to traumatic situations. As professionals, we have to take care concerning such issues in the best possible way, although they ask us not to tell anyone.

Little Ann came to my office with her mother because since kindergarten, she has been highly aggressive toward her brothers and sisters. I am Brainspotting with a stuffed Duck-animal, with which we do co-creative storytelling. She suddenly said, "The poor little duck always gets hit with the wooden spoon when she does not do what her kindergarten aunt wants her to do." I continued to listen to and asked if she had also experienced that. She expressed herself clearly, and was able to describe when, how, and even where she was hit. I began to add to the co-creative storytelling, saying that the little duck needed to be helped, and that I had done that successfully many times. Although she became scared about this reality, we were confidently working out a plan. I included her parents and removed the responsibility from little Ann. I thanked her deeply for her honesty because in sharing with me, she was able to help many other kids.

As with little Ann, I met many kids who opened with actual traumatic situations like abuse, abandonment, etc. The dual attunement frame allows the young ones to be honest and express their needs. We, as professionals, very carefully need to support them to solve the actual situation. There is hardly any way of integrating an ongoing trauma, but there are possibilities for coping well with actual traumatic situations. Managing an actual ongoing trauma better ultimately allows for less or even no post-traumatic symptoms. The individual capacity for coping strategies in trauma is often hidden deep in the brain and can be found and lived through a Brainspotting process. This is an enormous advantage of Brainspotting when working in times and places of crisis.

Young people, for example, feel that asking for help is the best protection if there are no possibilities of helping themselves.

Adolescents often feel ashamed about ongoing traumatic events. As professionals, we sometimes get into difficult situations. It is part of our responsibility and emotional frame to go into the fire with them and try to extinguish it. Sometimes we have to hold the hose together; otherwise, the fire would continue to rage.

A young man processes with all his confidence that a sports teacher from his school is abusing a friend. He witnessed one situation at a school camp, and no one else knows. Although he was not directly affected, a very close friend was the subject of the abuse. The sports teacher was well liked by the adolescents because his sports team was highly successful. In my professional helplessness, I asked the adolescent what he would do in my situation. I clearly explained my responsibility and that I was very worried about his friend and other adolescents. He kept looking at the pointer. His silence seemed endless. I could see that he was "fighting" with himself. Finally, he asked me, "Would you go to the director with an anonymous letter from me? My name must not be mentioned. In case it cannot be solved like that, I would also talk openly, but could you do this step first?"

I agreed. In this culture and given situation, I felt it to be a manageable response. The young adolescent did not have to go through a traumatic process while protecting his friend. Still, he could indirectly protect other young adolescents.

As a therapist, I felt the silence of the young man was endless while he was focusing on the pointer. What I described as "fighting with himself" might have been the neurological processes in his brain, held by the relational frame of waiting and giving him the time he needed to come up with a great idea.

2.3. Adaptations for Brainspotting with Children and Adolescents

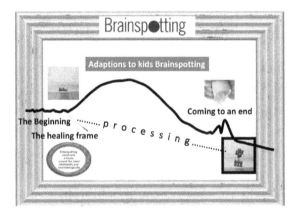

Figure 7: Brainspotting process visualization (Adaptions to childrens Brainspotting)
Baumann

Offering Brainspotting means to treat without protocol as it is believed, that the answer is in our clients. Following the so-called "uncertainty principles" brings true and long-lasting results. Being uncertain as a Braisnpotting therapist allows us to treat without prejudice and let us be surprised by our clients and their way of processing their trauma.

There are some basic guidelines like setting the frame, finding a Brainspot, asking for the body feelings, and allowing our clients to determine their way of processing by holding and adapting the frame.

In the following, it is described how some of the Brainspotting basics can be integrated into treatment of children and adolescents.

USING THE SUDS SCALE WITH KIDS

In Brainspotting, we use the Subjective Units of Disturbance (SUDs) Scale developed by Joseph Wolpe. He first introduced the scale to psychotherapy in 1969 for disorders in connection with fear. It has a value from 0 (no fear) to 10 (maximum fear). Over the years, this scale was integrated more and more into psy-treatments to verify how our clients feel during the treatments (Wolpe, 1969). In Brainspotting, we use the scale before the process begins. We ask how intense the body feeling or the emotions are on a scale between 0 and 10, explaining that 0 means no burden and 10 meaning that the load feels extremely intense. During processes, we can go back to the SUDs question to verify where they are as we work out an issue.

There are many ways of transforming the SUDs Scale to the appropriate age. Emotions, the thumbs up, middle, or down, hands showing a wide or small distance, etc. can be used. Kids around 10 years old mostly understand the question "How do you feel between 0 and 10?" as it is suggested by the SUDs Scale (WOLPE). The younger our clients are, the simpler the SUDs Scale can be adapted, down to simply thumbs up, thumbs down, happy smiley face, sad smiley face, etc.

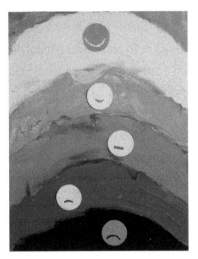

Figure 8: SUD scale as rainbow painting

This picture was painted by one of my very young clients expressing her feelings , years before I learned Brainspotting. Nowadays, I use it as a SUDs Scale. Colors (From Top down: yellow, light green, red, dark green, dark blue) and emotions are connected.

Kids tell me suddenly while Brainspotting: "Now I am in green" and I might respond, "Which one? Does this feel different? How does it feel?" I sometimes even end up using this painting to replace the pointer as kids start to process immediately when they find their feelings represented.

BODY FEELINGS

Brainspotting is a mind-body connected therapy. We assume that what is in the mind is stored in the body, and what is stored in the body is in the mind. Accordingly, BSP is seen as a physiological approach with psychological consequences (Grand, Brainspotting Phase 1).

If you have done Brainspotting Phase 1 training, you might recognize these phrases. Whenever I teach in a training, I try to emphasize the importance of the brain-body connection. For some of our clients, it is unusual to be asked, "When you talk about this issue, what do you feel in your body?" Most clients find a symptom representation in their body, independent of age and culture. Sometimes we help them to find it by encouraging them to scan their bodies or using other "hints."

I have observed that it is easy for kids to find body representations of their symptoms. They are still so pure, especially preadolescents. I ask them, "Do you have an idea where in your body the anxiety sits?" They show or tell you immediately. Sometimes I deepen the question, using my hands to symbolize. "Is it more in your head, in your chest, stomach, or maybe in your knees or somewhere else?" For kids, adolescents, and adults, it is true that sometimes they do not feel anything. At this point, I mention that not to feel is also a feeling. In the Brainspotting sense of uncertainty, I try not to interpret and to go from there, maybe saying, "Where do you feel it the least?"

BIOLATERAL SOUND

"BIO-lateral music was created by Dr. David Grand, the developer of Brainspotting (BSP), and is used as a part of Brainspotting therapy. It is hand panned to increase in volume in the left ear then decrease in volume before slowing increasing in volume in the right ear then decreasing, back and forth...rocking gently between the left and right hemisphere of the brain. It is intended to be played through headphones at a very low, almost imperceptible volume. Many people find it calming while also deepening access to the midbrain for deeper processing" (Randolph, 2020).

Kids and adolescents typically love this music. Their favorites are natural sounds like sea waves. For them to listen effectively, it is worth getting kid-appropriate earphones. When they want to know why I am giving them the music, I take out the brain model, which can be split into the left and right hemispheres. I explain that the left hemisphere is quite lazy when we talk about feelings. When the music changes its volume between the two sides, the left hemisphere is constantly reminded that there would be something to work on and in that way, both sides stay active.

ACCESS POINTS: ACTIVATION AND RESOURCES

Brainspotting is a resource model. The possibility of focusing on and, therefore, integrating emotional difficulties, post-traumatic states, blocks, or psychosomatic symptoms is an enormous resource by itself.

We can start a Brainspotting process on the activation model or on the resource model. It depends on how tightly we set the frame. The more kids are in a critical situation like treatments in hospitals, actual trauma going on in their lives, or even during a psychotic episode, the tighter the frame is set. The tightest way of framesetting is to treat only with the resource model of Brainspotting.

Mostly when I have decided to treat kids and adolescents in that way, they somehow worked out a personal event. They brought themselves into activation. I observe them wanting to get rid of the burden they are carrying. When this happens, I am sitting in front of them, trusting that their brain would know, and I am frequently surprised by their capacity.

As so often in Brainspotting, there is no recipe. Many examples using the activation Brainspot have already been shared in this book. The following is a pure resource case description.

Let me return to the hospital treatment of a 12-year-old boy. He was in critical condition with a chronic illness and had to have a painful intervention. He wanted me to come with him. As he knew Brainspotting, I talked with him on the way to the treatment room, explaining what a resource image would be like. He named a scene from Harry Potter, in which the pots are flying while Ron's family is cooking. He told me that he would imagine his pain to be cooked and that the pots would fly away as they would not be needed anymore.

Entering the treatment room, I asked him, "Where would

Ron's kitchen with the flying pots be in here? He looked up to his left. I managed to get him seated in view of the Brainspot. With the doctor, who was a genius in the way he treated adolescents, we shared the image. He went with us on this resource journey and always mentioned things like, "Now it must boil heavily, and now the pot must take off". This was great resource Brainspotting teamwork. The trust in the technique and trust in the power of a visual Brainspot allowed the boy to connect flying pots with less pain.

The decision between resource or activation model differs due to actual situation, age, and case. Adolescents are more like adults. Often they let me know that they are processing something challenging on the resource spot holding the silence.

Recently I saw a young boy, the son of divorced parents. He was here with his father concerning an actual very challenging time. He mentioned while brainspotting: "I prefer not to talk about that, because this is something I could solve with my mom, and we know how to deal with the situation." Before he said this, he looked at the pointer in silence for a long time, and I observed deep processing. For the father and me, it was an enormous release to hear that his mother was taking care of a very difficult situation.

Sometimes we also start with the resource model because we as therapists feel better doing so.

The decision to start with either the resource or the activation model is made up newly in each Brainspotting Situation. The openness to switch during the described models is the freedom of Brainspotting and allows this powerful treatment to become even more powerful.

OUTSIDE WINDOW, INSIDE WINDOW, GAZESPOTTING, AND SPONTANEITY

In his first session, Niklas was sitting on one end of my couch. His mother sat beside him. His father and I were seated in chairs opposite the couch. Besides getting general family information, the issue was touched upon. Niklas became quite nervous. I asked his mother if we could change places. From the other end of the couch, we looked in each other's faces. I chose a pointer with a football on top of it and asked Niklas, "When we talk about your issue, and you look at the football, where do you think the football should be?" Niklas pointed in the direction of my shoulder. I put the pointer there and checked the y-axis. As I found the Brainspot, I moved with my eyes behind the football, so that Niklas could have access to both the Brainspot and my eyes. He fixed on the football and started to talk about his feelings concerning the issue. A deep process happened, and Niklas found a way to be stronger in the near future. His parents silently watched and were surprised at how their 10-year-old boy could express his emotions.

Niklas' story is a typical spontaneous Brainspotting description. I saw him becoming nervous and used his actual activation to connect it with a Brainspot. He knew where the pointer would have to be, which I frequently observe with kids. I often move into the Brainspot with my eyes. Eye contact as an addition to the Brainspot can strengthen the relationship. Most of the kids seek the eyes of the therapist to feel the presence and to feel safe. For that reason, I recommend using a chair with wheels on the bottom. This enables the therapist to move into the Brainspot. Using eye contact it is recommended to reassure us if the child is fine with looking into each other's eyes.

A classic combination of inside-outside window can also be used. Kids and even adolescents often know spontaneously where their Brainspot is located. It can, for example, be asked during a play or a story: "Where would the hero sit, more to your right, in the middle, or more to your left?" Imagining the hero to be on the Brainspot, the process can be worked out.

With all age groups, especially with babies or kids who have no language, the outside window can be used to observe their body reactions, and trusting them, the professional decides where the Brainspot is.

All three basic techniques: outside window, inside window and Gazespotting can be successfully used with kids and with adults. Sometimes we hide them into a play or into co-creative storytelling. In the section on creativity, a lot of possibilities will be described. What is most important is to stay in the basics of Brainspotting, no matter which access we use.

THE POWER OF "MIX AND MATCH" FOR FURTHER TECHNIQUES

There are many techniques taught in the advanced Brainspotting trainings, you might ask yourself how to apply them when working with children. During the Phase 2 training, there is one slide pointing out the possibility to "mix and match" (Grand), which can be compared to "cooking without a recipe." As soon as we feel confident in the use of the basic techniques: outside window, inside window, and Gazespotting from Phase 1, mixing and matching appears naturally.

On one occasion, a student came to me after the kids' training and mentioned: "Treatments with the young population means not only to use Brainspotting, it means "being" Brainspotting. I thought long about this statement and really value it, as I believe it expresses exactly what we do (not only with the young ones): knowing the basics and integrating them as advanced techniques spontaneously and intuitively.

The Z-axis, meaning to create a different distance to the Brainspot, is most naturally integrated with any form of play or co-creative storytelling.

Sitting on the floor and having a pointer with a finger puppet in hand, while the child also has a pointer with another finger puppet on it, leads to movement. To stay on the Brainspot, the therapist's movements can be done along the Z-axis.

Another example involves "one-eye-glasses". Those of you who have done a Brainspotting Phase 2 Training know them. One eye is covered during processing. They are very much liked by most adolescents. Often the motivation is the technique of having something special behind them. Can there happen anything better, than having motivated adolescents?

While conducting remote work, double spotting, about which you learn in a Brainspotting Phase 3 training, turned out to be a great advantage, as we are not physically near our clients. One way of double spotting is to have a resource gaze spot set before you seek the activation spot. Finding a "resource gaze spot" in the beginning, connecting it with an OK feeling in the body, and having it there "just in case" allows safer access to the activation point during that setting. It serves like an airbag in a car or like good climbing equipment for high mountains. Clients of all ages reported this to be helpful to have at home even when the session was over.

Any further advanced techniques can flow into Brainspotting treatments. The best way to handle the techniques is to be aware of them and trust that the ideas of when to integrate them will come to you intuitively during the treatment.

RESOURCING AND EXPANDING

Dr. David Grand explained in a Phase 4 training that resourcing means to stabilize a good feeling and expanding means to awake in our clients the feeling that "they can fly!" Happily, in the child's limbic system, there are also many feelings stored that we really like and that are worth expanding.

Kids are still great in their fantasy world. Just stating, for example: "Imagine that you could fly! What would you feel? What would happen?"

You will get long stories and have the possibility to pass wonderful moments with children in your working areas by resourcing and expanding. Especially when symptoms are persistent and when the young ones have difficulties coming out of a vicious circle, resourcing and expanding can help to change their way of thinking. I highly recommend that you use resourcing and expanding with your young clients. It can be so joyful, deepen trust, and allow further activation and work out trauma symptoms.

In addition, you will enjoy your work as a therapist, and you deserve to have a "great fantasy session" too, which might bring you further into your work.

Me: When you look there, what do you think when you imagine you could fly?

Young client: Oh Monika, I would not need to stay in that stupid math class. I could listen from above. Yes, I would listen from the ceiling feeling light and weightless. I would not have to see that threatening look all the time from my teacher, facing me, expressing that I am stupid and that there is no hope for me.

I might even understand the content better like that. Imagine, I would be as good as I was before we got that teacher. Back then, I really liked math. I could even explain stuff to my older sister.

Oh yes, and my mom would not ask me all the time, 'Have you finished your math homework?' And, hey, I could focus more on preparing the oral reports I am so successful in. Do you know that I was recently praised in front of the whole class because I gave a speech about hedgehogs and did it well? The teacher mentioned that up to then, no one in the class had talked so lively and naturally about the chosen topic. I think I did not tell you yet how that felt. On my way home, I was still so, so happy. I had to run and jump just because I was feeling so happy. It felt like I could 'pull out trees.' And it was so funny that afternoon I was so quick with all that bloody school work. The whole world was full of colors.

2.4. Processing with children and adolescents

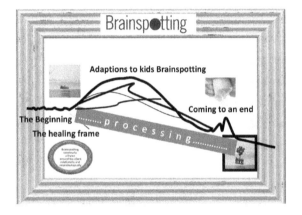

Figure 9: Brainspotting process visualization (Processing)
Baumann

Processing during a Brainspotting treatment can be so diverse from client to client. This is true for adults as for the young population. The possible diversity is expressed in the form of different "waves" in Figure 9."

Before focusing on the actual processing in this chapter, it is important to highlight our responsibility to act as Protective Professionals for children.

Adults are mostly more auto-responsible and have ways to take care of themselves, or we can help them do so, by offering Brainspotting.

A child, however, who lives in a traumatic situation, can not decide to leave his/her situation as an adult might. Children are extra dependent upon us and sometimes need extra protection to allow them to process with the help of Brainspotting. They may not even be able to express to us, their therapist, that they live in a devastating situation, as for them it has always been like that and seems so normal. This fully illustrates our responsibility to act as Protective Professionals for these children.

Providing this understanding and special protection deepens the relationship and, therefore, prepares a stable ground for profound Brainspotting processing.

WHAT DOES A CHILD NEED TO PROCESS?

Figure 10: Several sailing boats out on the lake
Baumann

Recently, on a nice but cloudy day, I was watching sailing boats on a lake. The wind was average force. There was one group of "Optimists," which are tiny boats for children. They were delightfully swinging over the waves. (see Figure 10)

Figure 11: Only one sailing boat left on the lake
Baumann

As the weather changed to a threatening thunderstorm, most of the boats went home, including the tiny Optimists. However, one seemed to be lost. There had previously been a storm warning and the little boat was still outside on the water all by itself with no other movement on the lake. (See Figure 11)

Figure 12: The sailing boat is pulled back to the harbor
Baumann

I was relieved to hear the noise of an engine and then immediately see a motorboat go out to the Optimist and bring the tiny sailing boat with a child in it home safely! (See Figure 12)

When we treat children, they should feel as if we are the motorboat: able to protect them and, if needed, rescue them. In a relational framework with children, in addition to mindfulness, an extra dimension takes place: "**child protection.**"

Our presence and being with children are essential. Trusting us allows them to go into their deep feelings as if they were being held by us. But what do we do if the young person opens up and tells of a current life-threatening situation like abuse or violence? Mostly, as therapists, we feel overwhelmed! Our limbic countertransference might make us helpless in the session. We might feel lost or frozen, being privy to information that hurts us as well. Our own helplessness is present in not knowing what to do or how to help this wounded young soul. Feelings of impotence accompany us as therapists.

Still, we have an extra responsibility in working with persons who are in danger. We must protect them in the best possible way, although there sometimes seems to be an impasse. "We need to be the motorboat."

Sharing your feelings is a form that kids profoundly understand. You might say, "I can really feel for you." or "This makes me sad." Through this method, time can be gained, and the therapist can sort out her/his thoughts. As soon as the professional is clear about what to do next, the situation can be discussed with the child or adolescent and explained in words they can understand. "The boat must be rescued."

At this point, kids might be thankful and "hand over the rope" to be rescued. Others heavily resist, maybe because the victimizers threatened them that something horrible was going to happen if they told anybody or other protective reasons.

Our presence in Brainspotting is so supportive. "Can you see where you feel the fear that you shared with me the most?" This gives us a chance to get into deep conversation and make clear that we are the "rescuing boat and not the thunderstorm." At this stage, I have had success sharing experiences I have had with similar cases, thus providing hope. I sometimes ask them simply, "What would you do in my situation, knowing that I want to protect you and trust that we can find a good way for you to move forward in the long run?"

One touching case I will use as an example here involved a girl who was approximately 7 years old and alone with her nanny when burglars came into the house and stole whatever they found. They put her into a room and tied her down so that she could not move and could only hear what happened. When they had taken everything away, they came back and raped her. The nanny turned out to be a friend of the burglars and watched the scene without intervening. However, the little girl understood what was happening, because she had listened to them while she was unable to move.

When her parents returned, the nanny lied and acted like a victim who had been raped. The girl's parents had no idea about the friendship between the nanny and the criminals. When we did Brainspotting with the mother and the little girl in a session, the little girl wanted to whisper something in my ear, and the mother allowed it. She whispered the truth into my ear, but the nanny had threatened her by saying that if she told the truth to anyone, she would have her friends come back and rape her parents and little sister and then have them all killed. As a therapist, I will never forget the wide opened eyes of the little girl when I looked into her face.

Instinctively, I asked the mother if she would mind waiting outside for a moment so that I could talk with the girl about her secret. She had no problem with this. When the door closed,

I got a glance of furious and anxious eyes. The girl crossed her arms over her chest and said, "Everything I have told you was a lie." With this statement, I imagined that she was protecting her family from the burglars' threats.

As a therapist, I felt helpless. Was she possibly seeking attention, or was what she said during the Brainspotting process true? Personally, I felt that it was all true. So, I sat down and while she stared at the floor, I told her the story of another client who has had something similar happen. Learning the truth, the family discovered that this other nanny was a dependent of the thieves. Together and with the help of the police, they arrested the criminals and helped the nanny start a new life.

The little girl looked up to me. I used one of the first Croco-Duck models in the form of a duck as a "pointer" in this session. She turned around, looking at the duck Brainspot and said something very touching. "You know what? I think we should talk with my mom, but I need the duck to have wings so that I can fly away if the situation gets really dangerous." We quickly fixed some paper wings on the duck and invited the mother to come back in.

Happily, the case was solved in the next few days. The parents were cooperative, understood their daughter, and fully supported her. I was right in assuming that her "lying" was self-protection.

Life became stable again in this family and the CrocoDuck, as you can get to know it now, has wings. I owed this change to the little girl and to all of us. The wings on the CrocoDuck always remind me to include another dimension in Brainspotting if I work with kids or adolescents in danger: a sense of protection and possibilities.

I have learned to take kids seriously, both in troublesome situations as well as in daily family situations, and try to provide or be the rescue boat if needed. I reflect on their symptoms with the parents or caregivers if necessary.

ACCESS TO PROCESSING VIA THE POINTER OR ANY OTHER MEDIUM

We treat kids in many different situations and can adapt to them and their way of being during treatment. Thinking about Brainspotting in a hospital during a painful treatment would mean accompanying the kid in the treatment room, looking for a resource Gazespot and using the kids' fantasy, i.e., what could be imagined there to endure the pain.

In private practice, we use completely different ways of offering Brainspotting. For example, sitting on the floor and using a finger puppet on the pointer is a method used to get access to the Brainspot. Children and adolescents love the pointer. They are also fascinated that looking at it brings up feelings. *What are you doing here? Is this magic?* Classic Brainspotting with the pointer is as possible as using a creative tool. Staying in the tail of the comet by adapting to the kid's situation opens many possibilities for "pointer use" or better named, "access to the process." More will be discussed in Section 2.2 on creativity. Our fantasies and those of the kids' allow for spontaneous and effective ways of finding the right access at the right moment.

NO SYMPTOMS OR DIAGNOSTIC - SPECIFIC BRAINSPOTTING TREATMENT

Students sometimes ask if there is a specific access for particular symptoms or diacnostics when doing Brainspotting with kids and adolescents. Therapists are curious if there is a Brainspot location for a particular diagnosis in one area of the visual field. They want to know where to put the pointer with specific symptoms, i.e., which distance would be the best for which set of symptoms. For example, does the pointer need to be to the right if the kid works out a very early trauma?

Brainspots are located by their relevance to the client's unique physiological activations, not to diagnoses from a manual. The uncertainty principle together with the dual attunement frame require that therapists treat each person in their own total uniqueness.

Therefore, there is no diagnosis-driven "recipe" for Brainspotting treatment. Daily experiences support and strengthen this belief. It is the uniqueness of Brainspotting for each client dictates the content of each process, and therapists are often surprised by the content. The openness of this model allows an incredible depth in working out traumatic situations and gives the treatment a special note. As a therapist, you receive many "presents" by allowing the deep and uncertain access supported by our presence.

Transforming the above question into daily psychotherapeutic life, I would ask, "Are the brains of Hans and Jane the same or different, even though they are both living with PTSD? Or depression? Or bulimia? Or "whatever" diagnosis?

Brainspotting is a brain-body related therapeutic technique. No two brains are exactly alike. Therefore, every Brainspotting process is inherently unique to the individual person. Just as with adults, there is no specific "recipe" for how to use it for "this" or "that" particular symptom with kids. There is only the possibility of adapting the Brainspotting technique to the given situation with each individual.

This possibility is, on the one hand, a challenge, and on the other hand, a joy when Brainspotting with kids. For example, a Brainspotting therapist can respond to one girl with bulimia doing paintings and replacing the pointer with the paintings, and respond to another girl, of the same age, culture, and language, also with bulimia, using the classical pointer, and help both equally.

"Do you think that the same Brainspotting treatment can be used for Juan from South America living on a farm and Hans from Austria also living on a farm since both are the same age and have anxiety disorders?" Or it might be asked, *"Do you think there is the same Brainspotting treatment for Jane from rural Iowa as there is for Maria from Detroit?"* The clear answer would be that the same creative techniques with the pointer (for example, putting a cow-puppet on the top) might be used, and similar questions might be asked. However, treatment requires observing and listening with all senses to their individual stories and body language. It is crucial to allow the flow of uncertainty and find the unique access point for each child's particular processing, regardless of whether their symptoms or backgrounds are similar.

Nine-year-old Jane came to my office because of her stuttering. We used the method of co-creative storytelling. I had a finger puppet on the pointer, and together we formed a story. Suddenly she said, "Wait, I have to think about what I want to say." She kept looking at the little puppet for quite a while, "thinking what she wanted to say," or better described as processing. She moved her head slowly, swallowed, changed her position, and continued to tell the story.

While I was in an Intensive Training with David Grand, we had a conversation about silence during Brainspotting, and I learned one important attitude: *"Whatever intervention we set as therapists during a Brainspotting process should serve to reach deeper into the limbic feeling."* When working with adults, silent waiting is an essential part of our Brainspotting treatments, and I enjoy that in so many ways. It means trusting the brain of our clients, not interrupting them, and allowing them in uncertainty to do their personal integration.

With kids, the phenomenon of silence is also observed. They also process during playing, being creative, i.e., activation. They might suddenly stop their activation to process or include processing into their play, talk etc. Some of the creative ways used while processing are described in detail later in the book.

The great challenge for us is to recognize these important moments and "catch" them. Having "caught" them opens many possibilities we have in the tail of the comet, like allowing silence, going with the play, doing co-creative storytelling, observing, asking questions, or setting interventions. As Dr. Grand said, "Intervene to come deeper into the limbic feeling."

Sometimes children process in the form of the "flight, fight and freeze mode." Why? Simply because they cannot sit in front of us and tell us: *"When I was three, I had to undergo surgery in the hospital and my parents were not allowed to visit me. I remember the nurse telling me that they did not want me any more..."* When we see them, they are still caught in their feeling and might not yet have the developmental state to talk about the past as something that happened to them.

Their means of trauma integration can be to react in our working areas as they reacted when the emotional wound first happened. Therefore, they might become extremely unorganized, hyperactive, sad, panicky, etc. to express their survival modus. Allowing them to present their "flight-fight or freeze" response in a safe setting, is one way a young brain can integrate what happened and therefore change their post-traumatic reaction.

I could observe this way of processing with children becoming extremely hyperactive or constantly running to the window or door or, for example, just sitting and holding Mom's hand while crying deeply without knowing why. When this happens and parents or caregivers are in the same room during treatment, I usually inform them about the good reason for that behavior. Like that they do not feel they need to educate the child during processing and do not disturb their young ones by working out something very important.

Sometimes it is assumed that Brainspotting with kids is amazingly fast and that healing goes quickly with this technique. Brainspotting (with kids) is actually "cooking without a recipe."

With the young population, any timeframe can be observed. Young children are still very "pure" in their way of trusting and believing. Sometimes this helps them to create rapid self-healing processes enriched with their fantasy worlds.

Very often colleagues ask, if processing with kids goes faster or if professionals talk more during Brainspotting processes with kids than with adults. There is no clear answer to this question. As mentioned above, there are the "quick processor kids," and there are children who can be silent for ages and do their inner way of processing. I invite you to think back to your childhood and a situation where you were happy to do something special. Can you remember how long it seemed to have to wait five minutes or how endless it appeared to wait for a special event like a birthday party, Christmas, or a performance in school? Five minutes for an adult might be an eternity for a young person.

Being aware of that, 30 seconds of processing for a young child might be as intense as 30 minutes for an adult. My general experience in the Brainspotting treatment with young ones is that they need less time to go deeper in their emotional processing and, therefore, seem to be "quicker." As already mentioned, it can also be different. It is important as a professional to be open for whatever is coming, whatever the young ones need is, and to allow yourself to be surprised by staying in the tail of the comet.

THE DOUBLE EFFECT

Independent of the symptom, very often the point of access turns into a resource point. The Brainspot where a child has an activated body feeling and is deeply aware of the threat of this symptom often transforms into a resource spot through deep processing. Learning this through Brainspotting brings about an awareness to have this capacity as a way of being.

When my three daughters were much younger, it was, of course, my responsibility to set limits. Sometimes I talked loudly; maybe too much so, and my girls did not like that. One day after such an event, they were invited to go to the Christmas market. They returned home with a gift they had brought me. It was a little wooden "jumping jack angel." They said, *"Mommy, whenever you shout at us, we will pull out the "jumping jack angel" and let you know that you could also be like an angel!"*

I hugged them for their cute idea. At this time of my life, I had no idea that this natural act from my daughters would one day be highly important during my professional trauma treatments. They taught me in a wonderful way that after or even during a difficult situation, the brain can find great ways to react. By the way, the little angel is still hanging on our kitchen window, while my daughters are already young ladies.

Several years later, I was trained in Brainspotting. A small group of therapists worked intensively with Dr. Grand. He was trying to explain to us that the activation Brainspot can turn into a resource Brainspot. While we were questioning him about that, he stood up energetically and proclaimed, "...but the point of activation is the resource point." In saying this, he stressed the word "is" loudly and clearly.

As soon as the client has a point of access to the activation, the client's brain is able to process and change the emotional heaviness of the activation into a neutral feeling. This reorganization of the neural network helps the client feel differently about the issue or symptom, and, therefore, the original point of activation turns into a resource Brainspot. Life stories and events do not change through therapy, but the feelings about them can change! We give our clients opportunities to allow and welcome everything that might come up, no matter how cruel it is. Allowing this processing is also a resource they may have never have accessed. Think of how often you are told during a Brainspotting process: "I have never shared this with anyone."

Fascinated by David's teaching, I was much more courageous to use the "point of activation," trusting the process, and often I could observe a resource feeling at the end of the session. I have never regretted this important learning step in my Brainspotting development. Looking back to David's jumping out of the chair from today's perspective reminds me of the "jumping jack angel" on my kitchen window. Although we as therapists might need to become like "little devils" (little devil is a warm loving expression in German, similar to 'scalawag' or 'wild child') in order to confront our young and adolescent clients with their symptoms, we turn into "little angels" when their point of activation becomes a resource point.

Soon after this conversation with David, I found myself in a children's home and in other projects treating kids and adolescents. One day a caregiver asked me to treat an unhappy, new little girl. She loved painting, so we expressed her depressive state by drawing dark clouds on paper. I used this image to replace my pointer and guided her to process her difficult life. At the end of the process, she mentioned that it felt like the sun and no longer felt like threatening clouds. I turned over the sheet of paper, and we painted the sun on the backside. Brainspotting the sun side meant strengthening her self-healing, and it became a natural resource for her. She left the session with the "sun feeling" in her body and her mind, also acknowledging that the cloud feeling is allowed to be there if necessary.

Recently I found an expression for this style of treatment: "double effect." I was writing an article for a German trauma journal. It just came to my mind, maybe like processing. I did not have to consciously think about it; the phrase came to me. This is how I often observe processing with kids on their point of activation access. Finding the right spot and having confidence in themselves, they give permission to process and, therefore, initiate the self-healing capacities and feel their lives form the "sun side"!

How does the double effect work?

I use little boxes, stones, cartoons, wooden spoons, etc. with two sides to replace the pointer. While I am talking with the child about her/his symptoms, we try to find a symbol representing the child's "unwanted feelings." Most of them are dark and threatening, like bad weather, a volcano, or a wild dangerous and aggressive animal, for example tigers or lions, or scary little anxious mice, a foggy landscape, monsters, etc.

Kids are so creative in detecting what represents their emotion. Having found a symbol, the kid can paint it on one side of the object. I use this piece of art replacing the pointer and the kids can go through their therapeutic Brainspotting process (finding a place connected with the body feeling, processing, etc.). The actual processing is still the most important moment of this treatment and means the classic Brainspotting is adapted to kids, with the integration of the traumatic experience in the brain as a less threatening event or feeling. When the kid or adolescent feels better, well, or relieved, I talk with her/him about the positive feeling and how it could be integrated into the young client's life. At this point, a symbol for the positive state of being is found and painted on the other side of the object.

The "other side" of the object becomes a "resource side" and can again be connected with a grounding Brainspotting process. The more I work with the "double effect," the more I understand that in its simplicity, most of the theoretical background of trauma therapy is included.

>The double effect allows me to show the kid that every trauma response, even if it is unwanted behavior, is a sensible, adaptive response. I share examples and explanations, such as the belief that a life without aggression would make it impossible to defend yourself if necessary. A life without anxiety would mean living unprotected or defenseless because anxiety can save you from doing impulsive things (like running across a street without looking or climbing up high old trees even though their branches might break). Any unwanted or unliked behavior is vital because it can "save" our lives. Kids (as

well as adults) need to learn how to use their responses to trauma in daily living. Can they really learn new responses to trauma when their brain feels in danger? Of course not, and here is another theory, which is simply explained with the "double effect."

>The child feels that she/he has no reaction other than the unwanted one: "not liked behavior," psychosomatic symptoms, anxiousness, being blocked, etc. Having the possibility to do a Brainspotting process with their symptoms, gives them the possibility to accept this way of being, or even to understand its importance, and it dissolves their "trauma state." This opens up good feelings, and suddenly they do not need their symptoms anymore to survive or protect themselves.

>Using the creative way of storytelling centered on a stuffed animal or a painting functioning as a pointer helps kids to feel much deeper what is going on in their brain. The younger ones in particular self-identify as the "hero" of the story. The main character represents their behavior, and so the change to the resource for them is profoundly real. Storytelling is often just the beginning. As soon as the kids are part of the story, they tell their own experiences, issues, traumas, and feelings.

>Another advantage of the double effect can be the presence of parents or caretakers during treatments. They can be educated to use the double effect object in the daily life of their child to help the child's integration of traumatic experiences. Like that they can for example let a child know dur-

ing being aggressive, that right now he/she is not in danger and therefore does not need the "attacking response" to a situation.

>Finally, it can be extremely helpful for the clients to be able to take the therapeutic object (pointer) with them. They are permanently reminded that all the change within them is now part of their daily lives. This is a simple way of strengthening what they felt during processing, a simple and deep way of grounding! The double effect object itself may also serve as a transitional object connected to the child's relationship with the therapist.

THE CROCODUCK AS ANOTHER DOUBLE EFFECT WAY OF PROCESSING

During my treatments, I developed a stuffed animal, which was very much loved by the kids. It is a little duck, which can convert into a crocodile or the other way round.

A little boy from a children's home (a safe place for children who do not have one) was very aggressive, but at the same time, he refused any assistance. He was maybe 4 years old and fairly new to the children's home. No one had an idea about his life story. The staff asked me to do Brainspotting with him. So, we sat down, and I asked him how he felt when he bumped his hands against the wall and pushed the other kids. He crossed his arms, looked ashamed to the floor, and replied silently: "Like a crocodile." Spontaneously I drew a crocodile on a tiny sheet of paper. Finding the outside window Brainspot I held it there to help him visualize his problems. He remained silent and contin-

ued looking at the animal. Suddenly crocodile tears rolled down his cheeks. Long moments of quietness followed. I held the crocodile paper in one hand and touched his shoulders with my other hand. After a while, he wiped away his tears, cleaned his nose, and stated with my prompting, "I could also be a swimming duck that quacks for help." I turned the paper over and drew a little duck on the back. After that session, one caretaker came by, and we shared the boy's idea with her. In the following days, the entire staff used the crocodile and duck to help the little boy. Any time he started to be aggressive again, they touched his shoulder gently and told him that there was no danger now and that he could also be like a little duck.

I loved the boy's idea and wanted to create a stuffed animal that turned from a crocodile to a duck and back. I actually wanted to develop a fundraising option for this children's home. If you would like to know more about this and its development, go to the homepage: www.varipets.com (Varipets). There are some teaching videos as well as some kids' videos in which they are the storytellers acting with the CrocoDuck. Dr. Grand is seen stepping into the shoes of a child. Last but not least, this page also talks about humanitarian trainings of Brainspotting around the world and how you can support them.

There are many ways to use the CrocoDuck. The yellow duck can be full of anxiety, hyperactivity, spontaneous, and the green crocodile can be aggressive, protecting its eggs while lying in the water and paying attention to what is going on in the surroundings, being lazy, etc.

Kids will give you many more ideas when you use it, as

they mostly project their stories into "Crocoduck." Brainspotting can be started either with the duck (anxiety, shyness, being hyperactive etc.) or the crocodile (being aggressive or lazy without initiative, etc.)

Figure 13: The CrocoDuck's transformation

How it can be used during co-creative storytelling, or to replace the pointer etc., is expressed in the following example.

Tom came with his parents to my office, wishing that he could be less aggressive. Asking about his means of aggression, I was told that Tom is a silent and lovely boy, but sometimes, completely unexpected, he starts shouting, arguing, and even kicking his parents or siblings.

After discussing his behavior, I took out my crocodile, stuffed with a duck, and asked him if he felt like a crocodile, at times observing a situation and then from one second to the next, feeling the need to attack. He confirmed my description and enjoyed playing with the little crocodile.

I started to tell a story and said that the crocodile also felt like he did but could learn to manage its behavior. The crocodile has learned that being aggressive is a vital behavior to defend itself, but it is not needed very often. Instead, it had learned to ask for help or to express its feelings.

The boy was concentrating and wanted to see how this treat-

ment worked. I informed him that I might need his help and let him know that the crocodile was sitting on a stone while talking about his bad feelings.

I asked if he had any idea where that stone was, where he would feel more like the crocodile: to his left or more in front of him or more to his right. The boy immediately pointed to his left. I asked him what he felt in his body when the crocodile was ready to attack, and he responded, "heat coming up my throat." Having this information, I led the crocodile along the horizontal axis to his left, asking him where exactly he felt the most heat in his throat. At a certain point, he tensed up and said, "Here. I would like to beat you!"

I stayed at this point with the crocodile and asked for his help. "Can you tell me exactly what you feel, and do you have an idea when this feeling started?" He told me that he felt very angry and like he wanted to hit me. It started when he was in first grade, playing football. He had the goal and the ball in front of him, but when he kicked the ball, it went straight to the left, missing the goal. His friends were annoyed and teased him. How could he have missed the goal in such an easy position? While he told the story, he mentioned that he felt "ashamed." He said at that moment, he turned red all over, causing the children to laugh more and call him "tomato."

I let Tom know that I was grateful to him and proud that he remembered so well where his aggressiveness came from and that he had trusted me so thoroughly in front of his parents.

Tom smiled shyly and said, "Well, I do not want to smash you anymore." At this point, I guided the storytelling and let him know that the crocodile on the stone was very sad and that suddenly an owl appeared in front of it, explaining that it could be different. The crocodile did not believe the owl and said that this would be impossible. The owl then asked Tom if he would help the crocodile and open the zipper on his stomach like this! Focusing again on the Brainspot, where the crocodile sat, he slowly opened the zipper, and WOW! In a quick transformation, the crocodile became a cute little duck.

Tom was fascinated and put the duck on his lap. He started playing with it. I took it back to the Brainspot, and we fantasized about how the crocodile felt being a duck that was no longer aggressive and very communicative with friends. We also discussed the possibility of asking for help or expressing his feelings using age-appropriate language. Resourcing for a while, I ended the story in the following way:

After a few days, the little duck realized if it would grow, so would its friends, and the crocodiles would grow and then get hungry and maybe even hungry for ducks. So the duck went back to the stone and asked the owl, "Could I be changed back to a crocodile, knowing that I can always behave like the duck in my stomach?"

I asked Tom where he would feel good now in his body and where he could feel the duck feeling best. He pointed at his stomach and automatically let me know that there were no more feelings of heat, and he had a new sensation: the duck feeling in his stomach.

To end the Brainspotting session, I took a little piece of wood and painted a duck on one side and a crocodile on the other side. He put this in his pocket and took it with him. Also, the parents can use the "Crocoduck" metaphors to help Tom when he needs to be more of the other one!

The CrocoDuck is also an example that explains neuro-biology. It does not matter which reaction a person has to an emotional wound, it is a good reaction coming out of the deep survival system. So being like the duck or the crocodile (having symptoms, behavioral issues etc.) means to be wise because the brain switches to the survival modus. Like that, it is expressed again how important the symptom is and that working on it does not mean getting rid of it; rather, it means integrating it into a way that it can be there when it is needed.

2.5. Coming to the end of a Brainspotting session

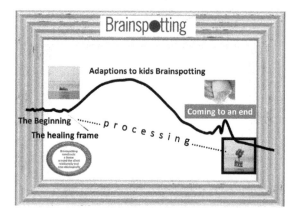

Figure 14: Brainspotting process visualization (Towards the end)
Baumann

GROUNDING

Planting a tiny herb plant in spring includes buying the seed or the baby plant, bringing it home, looking for an appropriate place where it would have the right amount of sun and shadow, digging a hole in the earth, and finally putting it into the prepared soil. Afterward, we cover the seed or raise the soil and maybe add a fertilizer. Watering is necessary so that the plant can sit firmly in place. The plant will stretch its roots deeper into the earth and simultaneously grow and become strong.

Grounding in Brainspotting treatment is a similar process. Our clients find the roots to a positive emotion or body feeling during a (resource) Brainspotting session. They then have the possibility to take it with them and let it get stable (roots spread). The long-time consequence will be that they get used to that positive feeling and expand it (the plant grows strong).

Kids and adolescents have great fantasies, and it is our duty to guide them so that they can access them. To provide some insights, let me share grounding ideas from young clients:

- A pink glitter liquid is running through my body.
- I am as strong as …
- When they shout at each other, I pull my head back into my turtle shell. There I cannot hear them, and it cannot affect me.
- My brain knows, so why should I think so much about it?
- When I feel that nobody likes me as a duck, I can be aware of the crocodile in me.
- Okay. I will ask them to help me whenever this stomach ache recurs.
- I will look up and imagine the rainbow, which protects me.

- When I am sitting in the swing, I can talk to my daddy and tell him everything that happens here, so that he knows what's going on while he is dead.

Earlier I talked about the double effect. Kids seem to have a natural instinct to believe in a happy ending. Again, there is a difference between young children and adolescents. While kids under the age of 7 or 8 can ground themselves greatly due to their fantasies, older – already realistic thinking young people - might need to be guided to a grounded feeling. This can be done through finding a resource Brainspot and focusing only on the positive feelings with all senses. In different trainings, we learn different ways of resourcing. All exercises that are used can be connected with a resource Brainspot. Positive feelings become expanded and deeply grounded.

David Grand recently started to teach the "expansion" model in Phase 4. It is worth booking a class and learning it.

"SQUEEZING THE LEMON", LONG TERM EFFECTS AND COMING TO AN END

"Squeezing the lemon" means to find out if children are easy to reactivate after they completed their process. As professionals, it sometimes feels like "fasten your seat belts," i.e., being aware that some activation might come up again. It is trying to reactivate them to see if the trauma integration took place. This can be done through imagination, serious questions even jokes etc.

At this point of the treatment, we might be surprised how strong our young clients feel at the given moment, or we get the information that there is still a lot to work on. When it is felt that at least some trauma integration took place, it is a challenge to find out which support to use with our young clients so that they can accept their life story or actual situation. This can be deep processing again or demand child protection as it was previously described in section 2.4: *What does a child need to process?*

It can be joyful when we receive creative, positive answers to questions such as: "Imagine you have to show your teacher (who was the reason for the traumatic experience) the strength you feel now. What would he say?" The general experience is that our clients feel much better after a deep Brainspotting process. To strengthen their work, it can be helpful to give them a symbol as a present, something that reminds them to keep the positive resource feeling in their daily lives. Coming back to the double effect, I typically give the object to the kids when they go home.

Anything like a piece of wood, a stone, a finger puppet, a saying (for adolescents), a message or picture on their phone, etc. can help them to remember what they have accomplished.

When you think back to the CrocoDuck story, all the caretakers in the children's home knew about the duck symbolizing the outcome of the Brainspotting session. "I could also be like a little duck, asking for help." They all used this symbol when the boy became impulsive or aggressive, and it was visible how much this little sheet of paper with the crocodile and duck on it, supported him.

CHAPTER 3

HELPFUL TOOLS AND ATTITUDES FOR BRAINSPOTTING TREATMENTS WITH CHILDREN AND ADOLESCENTS

3.1. The Uncertainty Principle - Sharing a special experience

Uncertainty for Brainspotting professionals means to allow the brain in front of us to develop its own best way of healing. One Trainer - Steve Sawyer - formed an expression to stay uncertain: WAIT standing for "**W**hy **a**m **I** **t**alking" and likewise wait before intervening too quickly. Te Uncertainty attitude gives our clients the unique possibility to find out their best way of healing and us professionals the unique possibility to be surprised by each process of how healing can take place. Whenever I work with kids who have not developed language yet, I am reinforced that Brainspotting is highly potent in its uncertainty. I do not know any other therapy technique, where in uncertainty post-traumatic behaviors or symptoms can be dissolved in such an effective way. As one of my students said once: "You only have to be there and wait..."

At this point, I would like to share a special case with you involving a 9-month-old baby, called M, whose family and hospital psychologist contacted me. All of us saw the Brainspotting treatment as a healing option in a helpless medical situation. We were extremely surprised by the outcome of the Brainspotting treatment. The mother and I wrote down our observations during the treatment, which you will read here. I use this possibility to enhance two different perspectives of the same treatment, which I call "trusting the uncertainty."

I chose this case as I believe it is a wonderful example to illustrate all the principles in this book. I want to especially thank M's family, as they all wanted me to publish it because they are so convinced that the Brainspotting treatment helped. After and during treating little M, I was also able to Brainspot with other family members who suffered from anxiety due to their experiences. Today I am happy when I get a message with photos of little M, who today is a happy kindergarten child, well-integrated with his friends, and no longer experiencing "near death symptoms."

THE BRAINSPOTTING THERAPIST'S PERSPECTIVE:

I received two phone calls concerning M, a 9-month-old baby. A colleague working in a hospital informed me that M had been urgently taken to the hospital three times previously. She was blue and appeared to be near death. Each time the clinic personnel could not understand why her oxygen levels were more or less in order, yet her outside appearance was indicating something different. The medical staff had no idea what the underlying issue of the repeated "attacks" could be, so they were open to an psychosomatic approach. Therefore, I was asked to give Brainspotting a try.

The parents informed me about this state and expressed their concerns. They explained their ongoing stress and strain, as M had not slept well since birth. From the first day, the baby appeared to have panic attacks between 10:30 pm and midnight. When sleeping, M closed her eyes but was screaming and sweating. The parents had found no way to calm the baby in these daily situations. They carried the inconsolable baby around, waiting for midnight when the panic usually stopped. I completely understood the parents' anxiety regarding little M.

When I first met the parents and M, we planned the Brainspotting treatment. To enhance our feeling of safety, we chose the hospital as the best treatment place. I planned to start only treating on the resource spot, setting the frame very tightly.

I met the mother and M on the treatment day, and the mother told me that she was very afraid. What a start! I checked with her to see if she really wanted the treatment and also checked with myself. I trusted the situation. We sat in the garden of the hospital on a wonderful spring day, and my colleague and I started to talk with M and her mother.

Little M was trustful that afternoon. My colleague and I had the baby in our hands, on our chests, and we even fed the baby. At a certain point, the mother started to talk about her traumatic birth and told us that the umbilical cord had been wrapped around the baby's neck twice. She mentioned that the baby had not been able to wear anything tight around her neck. Even during dressing, pulling something over her head or wearing anything too tight would immediately cause anxiety and panting for air.

While she was talking, I played with a stuffed animal – a little duck – and moved it along the X-axis. At a certain point to its right, I saw the baby's eyes freeze. I knew this was a perfect outside window Brainspot. I looked at the psychologist and the mom, and mentioned that I would try it on this spot. Within seconds, I let go of the resource spot intention. I took a hairband and put it around the duck's neck. I then slowly moved the duck to the baby and used M's little hands to help me remove the band from the duck's neck.

When M experienced that the first time, we all observed a deep, deep breath, then M gazed in another direction. The mother stopped talking, and we observed the baby gazing for about three minutes. It was impressive. The silence was powerful, and my gut feeling told me that something significant was happening.

After that, M turned back to the "freeze Brainspot" and kept playing with the duck. The hairband was taken off the neck repeatedly, probably ten times. The last time M took another deep breath. The three of us all felt the time was right to go directly to the unit. Treatment in which the baby normally cries was undertaken without significant difficulty and with a minimal amount of screaming.

The mother was very happy, and she felt that M was relieved. I stayed in close contact with the parents for the next few days. The first night M slept from 7 until 11 pm and then had a tremendous panic. The second night the panic lessened, and by the third night, M was sleeping normally.

I continued treatment with M and the family for about 18

more months. Anxiety due to life-threatening situations was not the only area in which Brainspotting was used. M later had swallowing problems of larger food bits. In one session I fed M while Brainspotting, which brought about eating without difficulties swallowing.

Today, more than three years later, M is a happy kindergarten child. She is nearly off medication, and medical control is only needed from time to time. The little duckling is still in her bed and very much loved.

THE MOTHER'S REPORT IN EXCERPTS:

Four weeks before the calculated date of birth, our child M was repeatedly found to have a decreased heart rate. From the checkups in the hospital, I was sent home and told there would be no danger. During the next control, the doctor diagnosed decreasing heart rates again. I was admitted as an inpatient for a close check but was sent home again, since the little one in the belly was being cared for and every day inside counted.

It was an enormous psychological strain for me, as I felt that something was not right. I felt that my baby was struggling to survive inside me. However, the doctors advised me to have further check-ups every two days because every day in the belly was important for the baby as long as it was being cared for. It was clear to me or rather to us that this was the case, but nevertheless, the concern for the life of our child was enormous. Two weeks before the calculated date of birth, the doctors decided to induce the birth because the situation was not improving. I just thought, "Finally!"

The next day, the birth was initiated. At that time, I had already had a bad case of bronchitis for two weeks, which was hard to deal with. I was having contractions, and suddenly the doctor shouted, "Your child must come out NOW! She has to get out now, no matter how long a contraction lasts. Take a breath while pushing, but she has to come out!" It was a horror. M`s heart rate dropped and kept dropping. I tried to push during the contraction, while simultaneously, but without success, catching my breath and managing the cough from bronchitis.

Then we did it! M was born. Her vital signs were completely okay again, and she screamed and wanted to drink immediately. Everything was fine. I asked what the problem had been. The doctor explained that the baby had the umbilical cord tightly wrapped around her neck twice. We were shocked. Was that perhaps the reason for the heart rate decrease in recent weeks? We did not get an answer. The problem with the umbilical cord was a fact that was no longer important in the eyes of the doctors.

I always had M skin on skin in my nightgown, nursing when necessary. As soon as I took M out, e.g., for changing clothes, her hands and feet turned blue, and her head became increasingly marbled. On the day of release, M was again examined very carefully. Shallow respiration was detected.

M was then transferred to the neonatal unit and completely checked, but no organic clues were found. We were discharged three days later with a monitoring device (heart, respiration) and caffeine drops. After ten days, these were discontinued, but we kept the monitoring device for M's sleeping phases. We never left M alone and took loving care of her.

M was a new-born baby who showed a constant "play of colors" in her skin. Three and one-half weeks later, we celebrated the third birthday of her brother. I wanted to breast-feed M, who was tired that day. M ignored the breast, and began crying very strangely. It was a crying that I did not know. I spoke with M and tried to calm her down. Suddenly, M was marbled from head to toe. First grey, then blue, suddenly it was almost dark blue-violet... I panicked. I ran into the living room to my father, who is a family doctor. Suddenly M was yellow. We put her on the monitor we had been using for sleep stages. Everything was fine. Dad immediately alerted the rescue team with an ambulance and helicopter. When the team arrived, M was very tired but stable. Everyone was shocked, and I was flown with M to the nearest hospital.

I held my baby in my arms, tears running down my cheeks. There are no words for this feeling. Thoughts were running around in my head. At the same time, I had to leave my other son behind at his birthday party. M was stable so far, and did not need oxygen. I was also allowed to breastfeed her because she was very hungry.

At this point, the mother reports the months of therapy in which M repeatedly had near-death experiences. These will not be described in detail due to data protection. What was noticeable were M's panic attacks. These and all life-threatening situations took place around the time when she was born!

Some of Mother's notes from her journal:
Spring :

"This was the beginning of Brainspotting with Ms. Baumann. We were in the garden of the hospital because of the danger of respiratory failure. With the help of a stuffed duck, Ms. Baumann performed Brainspotting. She held the duck in front of M, and she removed a hair tie, which the duck had around its neck, by pulling it over its head (= umbilical cord). When M had it removed, she took a deep breath; this action was repeated, and when pulling it down again, M was given a stethoscope to play with. This was hung around her neck without any problems. After this session, M fell asleep at 7:15 p.m. as usual. About 30 minutes later she had a terrible dream; again, again, and again she was confused and frightened, but for the first time she opened her eyes. What was different than usual was that at 9:30 p.m. she was sleeping deeply and firmly, which she usually did not do until about 12:30 a.m. We thought we had made it through the night, but exactly at 11:30 (time of birth), M was extremely restless, dreaming, and crying until she returned to sleep as usual at 12.30.

Throughout the following evenings, we continued the ritual with the duck by letting M pull the hair tie from the duck's neck, and we breathed together when she had removed it. Little by little, she began to sleep better. After having a cold, she reacted violently, but she never had to go to the emergency room again. Most of the time she even fell asleep relaxed on her back."

One month after the treatment, her mother wrote:

"Yesterday was another session with Ms. Baumann. M slept much more peacefully. She didn't cry in her dreams. She did not need emergency medication to calm her down. At 11:15 pm, she became very confused and cried with closed eyes. I managed to calm her down by talking and cuddling her. At some point, she opened her eyes, drank her bottle, and continued to sleep. She is still often awake, but now we have it under control."

Two weeks later the mother described:

"We had a control session again at the clinic. Today our doctor could measure the pulmonary pressure by means of heart ultrasound for the first time. There is no longer detectable pulmonary hypertension. The pressure is in the normal range!!! Everyone is indescribably happy, even our doctors. For the first time, our doctor said that it is unbelievable that M really seems to have had all the respiratory arrests because of the birth traumas she had experienced."

Another month later:

"Today we had our fourth session with Ms. Baumann. During the therapy, Ms. Baumann worked again with the duck "Lotte." This time she wrapped such a tight rubber band twice around her neck that M had to pull really hard on it. It was unbelievable. M breathed loudly again when she removed the band. She looks forward to helping the duck, and we will continue this ritual at home. Since eating pieces of food is very difficult, M is afraid of choking or cannot swallow pieces of food, Ms. Baumann fed M during the Brainspotting session. It was unbelievable to me. For the first time, our child ate as if she had never had a problem with it!"

First Birthday:

"Today is M's birthday, and we were again with Ms. Baumann. She has worked so well with M. Since the last craniosacral therapy, M throws her head backwards with such a swing, that she loses her balance and could hurt herself badly. This usually happens when she gets angry or tired. Ms. Baumann has worked on this problem with a doll. She also fed M again during the Brainspotting and worked with the duck."

Three months after the initial Brainspotting treatment:

"It's unbelievable. M has such joy while eating. She now bites off raspberries, soft strawberries, and nectarines, loves to nibble on bread sticks, eats baby biscuits, and today she ate rice with us for the first time. She no longer throws her head back. Meanwhile, I don't give her natural medicine falling asleep anymore. She drinks her bottle and falls asleep peacefully. Mostly she needs another two bottles at night. When M is awake and still has her eyes closed, I speak to her and tell her to open her eyes, and she will get her milk bottle right away. And it works! She has no more panic attacks in the night that startle her so that we fear a respiratory arrest. She still dreams often and a lot, sometimes very intensively, so that she cries in the dream. But as soon as I talk to her and cuddle her to me, she stops. She has made up for four months in the last month in terms of motor skills. She has made enormous developmental progress. M is a hero. What we really dreamed about is true, and we hope very much that it will stay that way."

I continue to hear from the family from time to time, always getting photos of "grown-up little M." Every time I hear from them, I am full of gratitude that I was allowed to offer what I have learned to love: a Brainspotting treatment.

3.2. Creativity

I once heard Dr. David Grand say, "Creativity is situated in the very deep brain. When our clients use their own creativity during processing, they are in a deep healing state." Staying in the tail of the comet with kids and adolescents allows us as therapists to follow the creativity of these young persons. Opening ourselves up and jumping into the kids' thinking worlds can be the most enjoyable, but sometimes challenging way of being present.

At this point, I would like you to return to your childhood. What did you really like playing, doing, thinking, dreaming about when you were an infant, a toddler, a child, a teenager? What were you "forbidden" to do or blamed for doing? Whatever comes to your mind now, be aware of it and try to keep it as a treasure in your Brainspotting attitude. These might be activities you can easily share with your young clients, which might help you to follow them wherever they take you!

Creativity can be integrated into Brainspotting treatments in various ways.

>Practically, integration can be achieved through acting,

drawing, dancing, playing, cooking, reading, doing sports together, being outside in nature, and so much more.

>In fantasy, we can undertake great journeys together. Diving into wonderland, creating stories, being strong against an offender, finding ways of asking for help, and so much more.

Whatever we do, wherever we follow, we help those young persons with difficulties build a strong inner world, a brain structure that not only allows for surviving but thriving a beautiful life.

To be creative does not require many tools, as kids still have access to their fantasies. I remember my mother making a dot in a tissue and playing Mr. Punch with it, while we four kids were for example in endless waiting situations at doctors or in shops. With a simple tissue, she made up wonderful stories, and we did not even realize that we had to wait for what felt like ages. Look at Figure 15 how easy this can be a Brainspot:

Figure 15: A tissue becomes a Brainspot
Baumann

Can you see and hear Mr. Punch telling us stories? Can you imagine him to be a Brainspot and helping kids to get rid of their post-traumatic symptoms? Especially in the children's homes, I have learned that every little stone, a piece of chalk, a simple paper, a wooden something, a little block, or even my pullover sleeve was good for Brainspotting processes.

SOME EXAMPLES FOR MORE CREATIVE WAYS OF DOING BRAINSPOTTING

Painting

Colors are a great way of expressing feelings. A white sheet, empty linen, or something similar can be used instead of a pointer. On this material, the upcoming feelings can be drawn while undergoing a process.

Painting can also be used to symbolize a resource feeling after having undergone a deep process. Wherever the Brainspot is situated, you can bring the surface as close as the child can work on it. Then a Brainspotting process with the help of colors and images can begin. While drawing, deep processing happens, and the outcome is a beautiful art piece.

How can this be done in practice? You can move the surface (paper, easel, etc.) along the x-axis until you find the Brainspot there. Then you can go up and down on the y-axis. Once the spot is found, you try to make the child aware that it should stay where it is (sitting or standing) and have the child paint - sometimes in front of the Brainspot, sometimes more to the right, or more to the left. "To paint on Brainspot" should be at a distance so that the child can paint easily. The z-axis is naturally part of the process, as kids move a little back and forth to look at their painting. Let yourself be surprised about the outcome and see that the art pieces I chose as an example speak for themselves.

One adolescent, after overcoming a psychogenic paralysis in the arm with Brainspotting therapy over months, felt the presence of a "muscle comic figure" to build up muscles again.

This young person used painting very often during the treatment. All the threatening and difficult pictures in his head could be expressed through the use of colors. I leave this muscle figure to your fantasy, as I have not taken a picture of it. Still, I was so fascinated by the idea.

Figure 16: Painting (Process: dark - happy)

In Figure 16 you can see how a young adolescent was accepting anxiety as a partner. This young client started with the little dark person presenting the anxiety and continued the process. The child ended up "being a partner of the anxiety" surrounded by a heart. After having gone through that process, the child painted only red colors on the canvas, to express the good feeling, having become a partner (left side of Figure 16). Both paintings hang in the child's room.

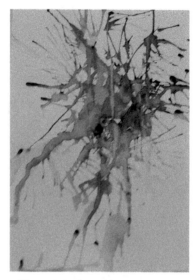

Fifure 17: Brainspotting process in a
watercolor painting

As you can see in Figure 17 very young children like to blow watercolors over a sheet with a straw. A 4-year-old girl, after a shocking event, used colors on the Brainspot. In this session, I was lying on the floor with her and looked for an outside window Brainspot. She was expressing her feelings by choosing adequate colors and by the way she blew into the straw, from really hard to smoothly.

Figure 18: Initially a Monster (Result of
a Process)

The monster in Figure 18 was looking horrifying in the beginning. At the end of the Brainspotting process, the 7-year-
old child changed the mouth to a smile, and it became a much
better company.

Blocks

Building a tower with blocks and finding out which block
represents the post-traumatic feeling allows us to process
whenever the child is ready for it. This is a suitable method
for kids who come and go to their processing like very active
or nervous young persons. The block tower stays in the room,
and the child can jump in and out of processing as their concentration span allows. As therapists, we can take care that the
child always comes back into the same position.

Figure 19: Boy with
blocks

A little boy – highly creative with blocks – came weekly, and we always found a Brainspot in his great buildings. It was a wonderful way to keep him focused and very helpful in integrating his experiences. It was so joyful to watch what he would build every week. Each session we found the "issue block" and "brainspotted" on it.

Dancing/body posture

A young girl sat on my sofa and talked about her sadness. I asked her if she could form a statue with her body, representing this feeling. She put her arms around her knees, laid her head on her knees, and stared at a red part of my carpet. She found a natural Gazespot by herself on which she could perfectly describe what she felt in her body. *"I feel sadness everywhere. My legs are stiff, my head is heavy, my eyes stare at this stupid red thing, and I am not able to move out of it."* Waiting allowed her to feel deeper and to share important emotions with me. *Suddenly she mentioned that her legs felt tingly, and she wanted to move like a turtle coming out of its shelter. I just let it happen. After a while, she moved around smoothly and asked me to play with her. We went into the garden and played "How does an active turtle feel."*

Kids can express themselves through their body language. They might be motivated to form a body statue to express their feelings. This "statue" could indicate a Brainspot where it is felt the most. This is mostly a Gazespot, as the direction where the "statue" looks is part of the body expression.

Likewise, a dance or any movement can express a feeling. When the child moves out of processing by doing something different it can be brought back to processing. The movement in between allows them to feel with body and soul, an expression for which they might have no words. During teaching, I started to call that way of processing "Hop on – hop off" processing.

Co-creative storytelling

Often young people say phrases like, *"This is like a..."* To take their ideas and make stories out of them, allow for wonderful and deep processes. Therapists can always ask the child how the leading character, who is often the identification of the kid, is feeling emotionally or in her/his body.

To give you an example, the child could say: *"When I am exploding, it is like a volcano. Lava is unexpectedly bursting out of the volcano mountain without anybody being aware of it before – even not me...and then it can't be stopped until it's over.* " Hearing that, the therapist could take the symbol of the volcano and ask in more details for it. At whenever it could fit, the professional could say: "Imagine the Volcano would be with us in this room, where would it be?" After finding a place, the child could be asked how it feels when the Volcano is with us now. Around that, a story could be formed with the help of the young client.

The child might tell the following to her/his Mom:

"The volcano came into Monika's office. It sat over there, and we both were really shocked. In the beginning, we hated it and actually were afraid of it. His eyes looked like pieces of charcoal, and his mouth was growling. It felt exactly like it feels, when I explode.

Suddenly the volcano started talking with us. I first did not want to listen as I was so afraid, but then I understood that the volcano could also be smooth – imagine Mom, it transformed into hot Christmas tea, with lots of honey inside. His eyes turned into shiny mugs, and his mouth seems to be like candyfloss...".

Reading stories

So many trauma stories can be connected with the right glance and questions like, "If you look in my room and imagine the hero to be among us, where would she/he sit?"

One of my favorite stories is from Chapter 16 of 'Jim Button and the Engine Driver' by Michael Ende (Ende, 2015). In this chapter, Jim (a young boy) and his grown-up friend Luke are in the desert. A huge giant appears, and Jim becomes full of anxiety. Luke takes him closer to the giant, although the little boy was full of fear and did not want to go nearer. The closer they got, the smaller the giant became. Standing in front of him, he was the same height as Luke and Jim and became a true friend.

I like to read this story to children alone or also in groups. I connect the issue with the giant. Doing that, I try to get them to imagine where in my room the giant would sit (Gazespot). Sometimes I take out the pointer and ask where they would feel the giant the most while moving along the visual field. Having found the Brainspot, I continue the story and stop whenever it is possible so that they can process whatever comes up. Sometimes I ask the young ones about their body and emotional feelings, or I am just present, being a silent observer.

"Stargazing: Talking to the stars"

This is a wonderful idea from the Brazilian/Australian Brainspotting Trainer Salene Souza. She invites the kids into a star bubble, and watching the stars allows Brainspotting.

3.3. Parts Work therapy with kids

Parts work therapy is found in nearly all psychological approaches. It intends to determine which inner part of a person is disturbed or traumatized in order to bring the emotional system into balance. Access to different parts, such as the inner family system, ego states, the inner conference (Schwartz, 2018) (Watkins, 1997) (Thun, 1998), just to name a few, try to heal destroyed or irritated parts with the aim of reaching emotional balance again.

Kids often present inner parts instinctively. *"It's not my fault, my voice can't be silent when it is shouting."* Statements like this offer spontaneous access to inner parts. As Brainspotting therapists in such situations, we can pick that "screaming voice" and ask the child what it feels like when shouting, and from there, go to an inner Brainspotting process. We can adapt all kinds of parts work we are used to into sessions with young ones. The best experience occurs when we take what they offer us.

Bad characteristics, symptoms, or behavioral difficulties, could be named "not liked parts."

Talking about "not liked parts" instead of "bad behavior" opens the possibility to determine what can be useful or important instead of blaming a kid for her/his behavior. *"It's not my fault,"* expresses directly, that the kid is not happy about shouting. Maybe negative experiences are the result because the surroundings are unpleasant when the "voice is shouting." However, shouting might be extremely important when we need to defend ourselves or "shout for help." Finding that out together is the first step in recognizing the importance of the "not liked part." Brain knowledge expresses that every reaction we have is basically a good, helpful, and necessary reaction. Our brain developed it because we might need it sometime.

The next step is to find out why the brain is currently using this far too often. Why does the brain feel in danger so that it needs to act out the "disliked part" permanently? Here Brainspotting processing is used as a highly effective treatment. We help the kid to either feel, verbalize, or express feelings about the unbalanced part. Starting to recognize the "not liked part" and finishing with the acceptance of it, and, hopefully, even beginning to like it, is what access to a single part allows in Brainspotting.

WAYS OF USING PARTS WORK WITH DIFFERENT AGE GROUPS

The very young ones mostly offer their symptoms directly as parts like "the screaming voice."

Simply asking them where in their body they feel it or asking them to follow the pointer (or a replacement) and letting us know when they can feel it the most, allows direct access to the part. Many therapeutic tools like emotion cards or pillows,

"Color How You Feel games", finger puppets, stuffed animals, etc. can represent the part and replace the pointer.

With young kids, the following exercise can be done: "Imagine that you have so many things you are doing well and some things you or others do not like as much; what would these things be?" A parts collection can be made up either with the kid alone or with the help of parents or caretakers. Then the place in the body where they feel them can be found. This can be done, for example, by drawing the child's outline on a paper. (The child could lie on a huge piece of paper, and the outline could be drawn for the child). This could look like the following picture:

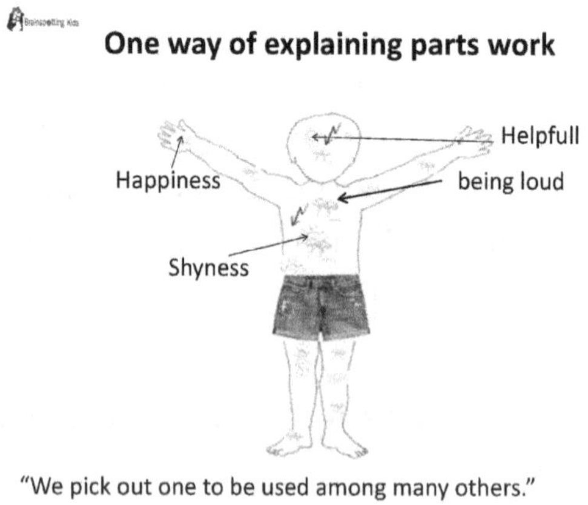

One way of explaining parts work

Helpfull

Happiness

being loud

Shyness

"We pick out one to be used among many others."

Figure 20: Drawing a child's outline on paper
Baumann

After finding out which "not-liked parts" might be important, Brainspotting can be started with whatever part the therapist and child choose. While deep processing starts, the other parts are holding and supporting the process, just by being present. This access can be transformed in many creative ways and be adapted to any age groups.

As kids become **adolescents**, they respond well to parts work as it is used with adults. Any adjustment that seems appropriate to an individual case can be an enrichment for Brainspotting work. Any age group may offer parts intuitively. My experience is that it is best to take what we are offered and "Brainspot" with it.

Shame and guilt are profound feelings. In professional literature, they are described as mostly having their roots in childhood. Applying Brainspotting to kids can mean meeting young people in times that they are developing feelings of shame. Addressing feelings of shame and guilt as internal parts of the kids means to step outside of the secret vicious circle. Otherwise, we would send the message that it is too shameful to discuss the blaming issue in therapy. Families and kids need to find places where they can open up with whatever is painful. It is not too much if there was sexual abuse, violence in the family, embarrassing moments, robbery with murder, etc. Brainspotting allows the space to share. The attitude of the therapist needs to support that in a gentle and safe way.

During the Brainspotting processes, kids are vulnerable but extremely open, and it is the therapist's responsibility to handle this vulnerability and openness with honest care. One way is to talk about it clearly and without fear. Parts work is extremely helpful, as kids are able to see their "issue part" as one piece of their personality and not have the feeling that they are "the shame." Suddenly someone accepts the child with whatever makes her/him feel ashamed. What a gift!

Another way is to listen and observe and show with our body language that we admire and love the child with the shaming issue. All this can be done during processing – with or without parents or caregivers present.

I received a phone call from a mother saying that she wanted to come in with her hyperactive daughter, who was 9 years old. The daughter would not be able to stay longer than ten minutes with us. We arranged to give it a try. The grandmother would be willing to wait outside and take the girl for a walk when indicated.

On the day of the appointment, an attractive, sophisticated grandmother accompanied her adult daughter to my office. The mother looked neglected, with bruises all over her body, and she was obviously extremely exhausted. They had Jane, the 9-year-old girl, with them. Jane was definitely hyperactive and had difficulties focusing on a conversation or one action.

I invited the mother and Jane into my room and started to ask for the family history. Jane, in the meantime, hyperactively checked out my room and pulled out games from my bookshelf.

To determine the issue before Jane would leave with her grandmother, I asked both, "In case I could help you, what would be different in your daily lives?" Jane jumped to her mother and demonstrated with her full body that she must not tell. The mother looked at me with desperation. I told both of them that it would be an important message and that I did not want mother to talk in secret with me. Jane looked at me with wide eyes while the mother pointed to her bruises. I asked, "Oh, Mom would not have bruises?"

Jane froze and stared at the floor. I bent down and tried to go into her visual field with my eyes. I said, "Jane, in case you are responsible for those bruises, I only want to mention that you are not the first child coming to me with this problem. Maybe we can find a way that mom would be able to live without blue spots all over her. Do you think you can help me?"

Jane defrosted and started running around again. I did not get an answer this time. When she left with her grandmother shortly after this scene, I took her hand and told her that I would talk with her mom and see how we could work this out. I asked her for permission. She nodded "yes" with her head and ran off.

Her mother described Jane's skills and positive characteristics. I wrote all those beloved characters of Jane on a sheet. During the next meeting, Jane was accompanied by her father. I then showed Jane and him the "beloved characters' list," and we chose one item that might be helpful to work on the "beating." The resource character was connected with a gaze spot to be there when we would need it. "Beating" was found with the pointer using an outside window. She mainly processed her deep sadness about being different due to her hyperactivity and having to have an extra teacher; these were some of the topics discussed.

After three weeks, I saw the mother again. This time she looked great; there were no more bruises, and she had taken care of herself. Jane's behavior had changed positively at home. Primarily, she respected her mom, and they started a healthier mother-daughter relationship. I worked a long time with this family, and Jane had many parts Brainspotting sessions. Her mother also processed why she was not able to set positive limits for Jane. After getting to know the mother's own traumatic story, I could completely understand her helplessness in educating Jane. (This was one of the cases in which I used the "frame in frame" model.)

This was one of my most intense Brainspotting family works. I was able to get in focused communication with Jane. After several months, I realized that she did not feel shame anymore about having been so aggressive toward her mother.

I am fairly certain that one of the most critical steps to the success of this treatment happened in the first meeting. I talked directly and openly to Jane about beating her mother, even though she felt so ashamed about it that she froze. I moved into her frozen look to demonstrate to her that I liked her as she is. Finally, I motivated her to work with this shame part, recognizing that there are many more positive parts in her life, and asked for her cooperation.

"The child in me" as a form of the inner part

Working with the inner child is a traditional therapy method. You can find a lot of literature on how to "heal the inner child."

Without knowing any of that literature, you will observe that your clients, during Brainspotting processes, talk about situations when they were much younger, even babies. Very often our clients feel like they want to meet their inner child, and it happens automatically during processing.

Recently I had such an adolescent client. He was looking

at the pointer and stated, *"I can actually see myself in that situation. It must have been before I went to school. I think it was on a Sunday after church. We were all sitting in the kitchen...I felt so alone, nobody gave me even a glance of attention. If I had just had somebody who would have seen me." Here I only asked if the young child can feel that the grown-up self sees the kid. The adolescent indicated that the young child could see the grown-up clearly. In his mind, he also went into that kitchen and took the little boy – himself – away, and they spent a fun day together.*

In this example, meeting the inner child in connection with an inner part happened automatically. The inner child treatment during Brainspotting is observed to be extremely effective. Again, I return to the saying of David Grand, "Every intervention we do, we should only do to come deeper to the brainstem..." Using the inner child can be very helpful in reaching deeper processing. It can also be used with very young children.

Recently I saw a four-year-old, a very smart kid, who took out a little doll and processed while taking care and cuddling the little baby, telling me, "You know, I had to be in the hospital for a long time when I was little, and my parents could not always be with me."

Inner child work is also very effective when we see clients for a single session. For example, when we treat parents who suffer with their traumatized kids or who use "educational" methods, such as violence or shouting, and we cannot support their way of educating. Typically, the parents were treated similarly when they were young, and it helps them to heal their trauma and change their behavior toward their children. The inner child technique can be extremely supportive in this context.

There are so many ways of "meeting the inner child." As described above, it can just happen during the session. David Grand also shows a video in Phase 4 where this can be seen. We can also ask for the inner child to come into the room: *"Imagine your little self in that situation who would sit outside this working place in the waiting room. Would you like to invite her/him in?"*

The client can also go into the situation where the trauma happened. *"What would little you feel, if you as a grown-up today, were with her/him?"*

As Brainspotting therapists, we remain in the uncertainty principle and are surprised to discover what is going to happen. Your clients, even the young ones, offer much more access to the inner child than could be described here. When we treat very affected traumatized people, it can take many sessions until they can even look at their younger self.

To stay in uncertainty principle is important so our young or older clients can integrate their life stories, as their brains are capable of doing. It can feel good when a client can hug their inner child. Sometimes just accepting it is a more impactful step.

In using the inner child technique as an intervention to gain access to deeper brain processing, I have experienced that it is better not to ask about a specific traumatic situation. I ask my clients, adapting my language to their age, when they think back, which was the most challenging, most burdening moment around a given situation. Typically, I get immediate access to their most traumatizing feelings, which are often worse than the actual traumatic event. For example, a child trusts someone beloved and asks for help, and this person does not answer the need, in effect, disclaiming the need, or having to watch a loved adult, like a father or mother, violently abuse a sibling or partner.

Brainspotting, in its openness, allows access to whatever was the most incriminating to the person's emotional system, which is in front of us and asking for treatment. This way of treatment can easily be adapted to children from a very young age through adolescence. Questions such as, *"When you think back, to ... "* and *"When you look back, which was the worst moment?"* or questions like: *"Imagine you could see yourself in a film. When did you suffer the most?"* With very young children, it is sensitive to ask the same questions in a language where they can connect with their young self directly, such as, *"When you think back to little Amy in her blue dress, and you imagine her, what was the worst moment...?"* or *"Imagine you could see little Amy with her blue dress in a film. When did she suffer the most?"*

Connecting these questions with Brainspots, as you have read in so many ways in this book, is a powerful help to allow deep processing for our clients from a very young age to even old age.

3.4. Setting

In psychotherapy, the question of setting differs from school to school. While my Austrian "therapeutic grandfather," Sigmund Freud, had his clients lie on a couch in each session, approximately 70 years later, I learned systemic family therapy in the same city. One type of therapy exclusively treated the symptom carrier. The other taught me that the symptom carrier plays a role in a system. These two different attitudes of therapeutic accesses are both helpful for people with emotional healing needs.

One of my favorite PowerPoint pictures from the Phase 1 training states: "BSP is an open, creative, integrative model. It is designed to be adapted to any clinical approach and therapeutic style. There is no turf when it comes to healing! (Grand, Brainspotting Phase 1)

There are many possible Brainspotting settings with kids and adolescents, and most of the time, you can decide spontaneously what would best fit in the current session.

Sometimes it is important to have caregivers or parents present, and sometimes it is preferable for them to wait outside the treatment place. The same is true for siblings. It is not always easy to find out which setting would lead to the best outcome. Obviously, the younger a child is, the more a close relation is needed.

Recently I was informed that a father would come with his daughter to my office. When I opened the door, there was the little girl, the father, the grandmother, a social worker who accompanies the family in daily life, and a sibling. I invited them all into my office but felt completely overwhelmed by the number of people in my small room.

I started to get the family history. The young girl was very self-assured and took over the conversation. She told me everything about her family, why there were so many people accompanying her, and that she needed treatment because she suffered from post-traumatic symptoms. At this point, I was again overwhelmed. She knew so much at her young age. I asked her if I could work with her for ten minutes alone. She agreed, and she was able to process deep emotions with the brain model. At that point, I explained to her where the fight modus was coming from.

After this ten minutes in which so much happened, all re-entered, and I determined the setting that would be best used in the future. All agreed that the best circumstance would be to work with the grandmother and the girl. The reality was that the grandmother came only once, and I primarily ended up with the girl and her father. It was a very special time for all of us. The setting was adapted each session, and I learned to be without expectation as to who would arrive for the sessions.

When choosing the setting, it is important to take care of

a stable emotional frame, which allows people to process their issues. It does not matter who is present in this emotional frame, as "there is no turf when it comes to healing." I observed it to be less important to take care of the surroundings, such as silent rooms. This might be more important for therapists. When trusting kids, the trust is everywhere, e.g., in a loud children's home, on a schoolyard with children playing, in front of a grave, or in the surgery room of a hospital, to name just a few locations where I had great Brainspotting sessions.

Sometimes we have nothing more than presence and the ideas that we have heard about in Brainspotting. Independent of the setting, during an acute crisis, when kids are extremely hurt, taken away from their parents, full of loss, etc. due to an acute situation or often due to limbic countertransference, we can do nothing more than be present. My experience has been that this is so much! Whenever a Gazespot occurs in such a situation, either with an individual or a group of people, it's worth catching it! It can be named, and the affected person can be guided to it. Often it helps to either calm down or even work out old traumas unconsciously.

BRAINSPOTTING TREATMENTS WITH CHILDREN AND ADOLESCENTS REMOTELY

As I am currently finishing this book during the COVID-19 pandemic, it allows me to mention a YouTube video, which I have done with two very competent colleagues in English and German, "Telehealth Treatments with Kids and Adolescents during COVID-19 Times." (Baumann, Sulek, & Tomek, YouTube, 2020).

During these times, my experience grew in offering online work with this young population, and I am still surprised how well it works. It is assumed that most readers have conducted remote therapy sessions due to COVID-19 circumstances. For those who haven´t, the above free YouTube video is recommended.

In the following list, some Brainspotting tips and general "likes" from my experience are provided.

- Try to have an "easy to move chair" and either Bluetooth headphones or loudspeakers so that you are able to move further away from the screen. It can be important if you work with the pointer (sometimes with finger puppets on it). Moving back means that the X-axis becomes wider.
- Hyperactive children are more focused when the headphones have a cable to the computer.
- With young children, I changed the setting to twice a week but reduced the time to only 25 minutes, as the concentration span seems to be shorter when they are in front of a computer.
- Roleplay works great. The therapist can use a finger puppet on the pointer, and the child can use a beloved stuffed animal, play tool, etc.
- To symbolize the feeling, a Post-it note can be fixed on the pointer and a symbol drawn on it. In this way, the double effect can also be practiced.

- Using "double spotting" where you have an activation spot and a resource spot, allows safe access.
- Children can proudly show their way of living and bring their beloved things in front of the screen.
- When treating younger children alone, always have the phone number of a responsible person in the home. There might occur a moment when they are needed – sometimes only to hug the young ones or to bring tissues.
- Always assure yourself who else is in the room.

In one session with a young lady, after about 40 minutes, the head of the little brother jumped up from under the table and stated, *"No, no, that is not true."* I was glad that in this session, we had not done any deep trauma work. I learned to ask the kids if someone else was in the room. By the way, the young lady, the younger brother, and I gave this bizarre situation a big smile.

"FRAME-IN-FRAME" AND SYSTEMIC INTERACTION

When children are affected their families or caregivers often suffer with them. Vice Versa it is also true that children might suffer when somebody in the safe system has a serious problem. The following case example taught me that treatments with more than the affected child can be of great help.

I had an appointment with a mother and her 8-year-old daughter. The therapy aim was to help the daughter with serious anxieties. The facts behind the symptom were the following: A year before that session, the mother had been hit by a car and seriously injured. Her situation was highly critical, and she was in the hospital for a couple of weeks. After the mother recovered, the girl presented anxiety symptoms, such as sleeplessness, fear of being alone, and increased shyness.

During our first talk, the young client started to fix on a Gazespot, and without much explanation, I put a picture marker on the wall and asked her to continue looking at it. She did a natural deep and emotional Brainspotting process while I was present. Sometimes I glanced at the mother and observed her becoming frozen during her daughter's process. She turned pale, and desperation was visible on her face.

After the girl finished and felt released, my first intention was to turn to the mother. I shared my observations with her asking, "Has your daughter's way of sharing her feelings affected you right now?" The mother indicated that it was hard for her to hear the feelings of her daughter, but she believed that this was important. Having seen clear brain-body connection and activation in the mother's body language, I offered her a Brainspotting session on another day. The mother wanted to think about it but had no time. The little daughter jumped up, touched her mother's shoulders, and said, "Mommy, that is so good! You have to do that! When you do that, I will sleep better for sure."

Soon after, I had an excellent session with the mother, where she shared her emotional wounds and physical difficulties after the accident. These challenges still influenced her daily life. More than five years after this session, her symptoms are gone. As you can imagine, the daughters' anxieties also disappeared. I had some additional sessions with the daughter years later, focusing on when she was an adolescent and confronted with two people dying in her personal surroundings. She is a great teenager nowadays.

This case taught me a significant lesson in my work with kids and adolescents: *"Mommy, that is so good! You have to do that! When you do that, I will sleep better for sure."* This direct and clear message out of a kid's mouth opened my mind. When parents or somebody close has to go through difficult and possibly traumatic moments, the kids are often "co-traumatized" or "hidden traumatized." This is also true when a child is hurt or does not behave as usual. The parents are affected and are truly thankful for Brainspotting help. As I also treated the mother in this case, I could see how effective it was to work with both mother and daughter around the same issue. I repeated this often and with great success.

One important setting point is that I often treat kids with their parents present for support. I never treat an adult with the child present. Kids could be traumatized by hearing and feeling what their parents have gone through in their lives. This is not only true when parents suffer with their kids. Violent parents often have been victims of the same upbringing. When a child comes up with an issue around punishment, aggressiveness, or abandonment in the family, we can suggest that the responsible and affected grown-up get a Brainspotting session working around her/his way of educating. Focusing on how they feel (or maybe felt) setting limits in an unpleasant way. It is amazing how changes are possible if one's personal and often sad story is worked out.

Realizing the strength of Brainspotting with a larger frame

made me think that I should call this "frame in the frame in the frame." Visualizing the picture, it looks like this:

Figure 21: PowerPoint from the three-day "Brainspotting for Kids and Adolescents" Training, 2019
Baumann

When a child is recommended for treatment, we realize that the parents or caregivers are also affected and offer them treatment, too. This can be done either with us or with another Brainspotting therapist, depending on the situation. Sometimes the system of those affected gets larger and may involve school, teachers, doctors, etc.

This leads to the next setting title:

THE COMMUNITY TRAUMA

Trauma in a community spreads trauma reactions among a large population. Some people are directly affected, while others know affected people and feel helpless or guilty about what has happened.

When I had the honor of teaching a Brainspotting training together with Dr. Martha Jacobi and Dr. David Grand in Sandy Hook, Connecticut five years after the school shooting, I remember having read above the entrance to the Trauma Center a saying from David Grand expressing: "We are traumatized alone, but we are healed together."

This phrase has stayed with me since that time, and I can genuinely confirm it.

I have been present in completely different traumatic community situations. My personal conclusion of what is most needed during treatment in a community tragic situation is detailed below:

> **Our presence**

> The possibility to **ask for support** or help as a professional to handle our being affected as professionals, too.

Being present when trauma actually occurs is the core piece of Brainspotting treatments in these situations. On the one hand, the affected persons have the feeling that a professional is with them, somebody who can offer them safety to whatever reaction they are having. The professional will accept them and take care of them if necessary. On the other hand, knowing that presence is so important and already a major part of healing lowers our expectations as professionals.

All that we offer is our being there and allowing us to develop what is needed or accepted. In these acute situations, I have never had a pointer with me. However, I was aware of Gazespotting and the resource model somewhere in my mind. In these situations, my clients individually and spontaneously gazed, and I just guided them to stay with their glance wherever they felt it to be best at the given moment. Being present is the entrance to Brainspotting treatments with individuals or with a group of affected (children) during a crisis situation.

In the role of a therapist, feelings of helplessness or insecurity are normal. The openness **to ask for support** is essential if possible. It is highly recommended to stay in contact with colleagues. This dialogue helps tremendously to lower our trauma reactions. During the COVID-19 pandemic, a team of Brainspotting therapists offered treatments to each other. It was reported as extremely helpful and allowed us to function in a situation in which we were also deeply affected. It brought back the capacity to treat and, therefore, allow for healing.

I was sitting in the middle of a community tragedy. People told the affected kids, "Please see Monika. She is a professional." Honestly, I had no words to offer, only the volunteering of my presence. After mentioning that I would be there and willing to interact with the affected children, I simply waited. After about an hour, one of the affected children came up and took his place beside me. He started talking and talking and talking. I was told about wonderful situations during his earlier childhood, which would not be possible anymore. Then the boy started to go through all the traumatic situations from the night before, which would change his life drastically. He stepped into the situation again and shared details. All I did was be present, put my arm on the child's shoulder, and support the visual fixing of a piece of chewing gum on the floor. After about 90 minutes, he brought himself into a resource future, sharing what he would do differently when he becomes a grown-up.

I was surprised how this young boy started with resource events from his childhood, coming to the actual trauma and finally creating a resource future. This is a natural way of Brainspotting – again teaching me how important it is to WAIT.

After this very touching sharing and when I felt I could leave the situation, I called my Brainspotting friend, Dr. Martha Jacobi, and shared my feelings of being frozen, asking if I could do something else for this family. Martha reflected on all the steps I undertook on the phone and gave me the feeling that I took the best possible action in this situation, especially supporting his gaze on the chewing gum. This was my way to get out of my affected state and to allow more presence in this community during the following days.

In another situation, I was called by employees from different departments of a countryside school. The school is situated far away from any psychological help. The traumatic death of a schoolchild had occurred. Listening by phone to the responsible people in the school, such as teachers, the headmaster, and the parents, allowed me to speak through a "telephone presence." What are you looking at right now? I simply mentioned that they could choose to stay there with their glance, as this might help them to concentrate. Just recently, about five years later, one of the affected teachers in a Brainspotting training reflected how powerful it had been for her to be sent to a resource spot while talking on the phone with me, without realizing that I had done Brainspotting with her.

Treatment in a community, which has recently experienced trauma is hugely different from treatments if the trauma is currently occuring. . Dr. David Grand and Dr. Martha Jacobi have volunteered Brainspotting treatments for years in Sandy Hook, Connecticut, after the tragic events at Sandy Hook Elementary School on December 14, 2012. In this terrible situation, 26 individuals were killed and Brainspotting was found to be the most powerful treatment. You can find out more information on this in the "Report of Findings from the Community Survey September 2016" (Newton Sandy Hook Community Foundation, 2016).

Given the possibility of offering Brainspotting treatments after trauma in communities, this technique can be implemented in groups as well as with individuals of all ages. Writing this text, I find myself after the first lockdown in the middle of the COVID-19 crisis. It has been observed by many of my colleagues and me that actual trauma awakens our old trauma responses, which can be described as post-traumatic reactions. Brainspotting can be seen as a chance to dissolve even old blocks after traumatic events.

Finding the Brainspot means allowing our body and emotions to express the post-traumatic state and to potentially dissolve very old blocks. This helps us to live the reality and to get out of a natural dissociative state. It enables us to act in the "here and now" and to come back into the present life.

People do react with many different post-traumatic symptoms, such as anxiety and sleeplessness, after a community trauma. Being present and giving children the chance to Brainspot – the chance to believe in themselves and to go forward with whatever happened to them – supports healthy brain development and, therefore, the capacity to live in the "here and now".

With kids in individual treatment, you can work as described in this book. Kids find their way of integration through Brainspotting. It does not matter if you use creative techniques, classic Brainspotting, or any access that offers the possibility of awakening the self-healing process. Furthermore, it does not matter whether you treat in the presence of parents, caretakers, or individually.

BRAINSPOTTING WITH FAMILIES OR MORE THAN ONE CLIENT AT THE SAME TIME

To use Brainspotting with more than one person during the same session is a powerful way of treatment. It is worth a try and can be smoothly included in a session.

In the context of this book, there is usually at least one adult person present and at least one child or adolescent. They are coming to our workplace because an issue exists. Asking about the issue activates them. When there is activation, it can be the right moment to offer Brainspotting. This can be done with the pointer, and you work with two pointers, or you ask for Gazespotting or even a combination of the two. Again, the indication to Brainspot differs from young kids to adolescents.

You could, for example, ask younger children with their

parents, *"Imagine there would be a TV in this room. Where you could watch or feel really focused about putting it? Where would it be?"* With adolescents, a short description of Brainspotting could be given, and then look for the Brainspot.

Having each individual find his or her Brainspot helps your clients to focus on their feelings and allows you to guide two – maybe three or more processes for other people at the same time. Surprisingly, the processes often enhance each other, or one causes the other to come forward.

Two short examples will deepen your understanding of this process:

M, a 7-year-old, came into my office with her father. M had gone through a terrible school situation a few days ago. She immediately began to cry when she and her father talked about it. I asked her to find the imaginative TV in my room so that she could best talk about it. She chose a spot in a corner. Her father was also guided to find a place on which to focus, where he could best endure his daughter's telling of the story. He decided his daughter would be the Brainspot. He mentioned that he just wanted to look at her.

We all listened to the girl's trauma work, and at the end her father stated, "Now I can suddenly feel my body again. I did not realize that I had been so stiff since this happened."

A father came in with his 17-year-old son. They had suffered a significant loss in their family some months before. Soon after the first lockdown of COVID-19, they could not cope with the situation. After explaining Brainspotting to them, I asked them to find their gaze spot. They looked in completely different directions. Both could process their emotional pain in connection with their loss, their helplessness, etc. One started speaking, and the other person added his feelings. In that way, each of them could process in the presence of the other, and, in the end, they found a resource spot, on which they felt really well, together.

Offering Brainspotting to family members who are, for whatever reason, in a conflict together is a great challenge. Instead of "scratching each other's eyes out," they get the chance to process on their spot and give a solution a chance.

BRAINSPOTTING TREATMENTS IN GROUPS WITH CHILDREN AND ADOLESCENTS

There are many ways of offering group therapy to young people. Currently, the Ecuadorian Brainspotting Trainer, Glenda Villamarín, is offering a three-day training about Brainspotting with groups, and it is well worth taking.

Concerning young ones, Group Braispotting is often used with two or more adolescents in clinics or for follow-up therapy. Resource work can be an easy step toward Brainspotting with groups. Each one can find a resource – a gaze spot for a certain topic, and an interchange can follow. Using activation points with groups of young persons should be carefully prepared in advance, as it might be an intolerable challenge to hold more than one or two activated persons therapeutic helpers might be needed.

Besides having the group of young people seek a Brainspot, you might also put an object in the room and ask everybody to search for the best activation/resource place. Young people can observe their own body feelings while they walk around in the room looking for the object. Each individual can choose the place with either the highest resource feeling or the highest activation before starting Brainspotting together. The following case description is one example of Brainspotting with groups.

I was asked to come to the children's home urgently because one person had a psychotic episode and ran away in a very unpleasant way. The children between 3 years and 18 years of age were shocked. It was already bedtime, a time when they usually sit together singing and praying. I stayed with them during their daily ritual and proposed to tell them a story at the end. To listen to the story, I asked them to choose a place on which they could sit, feel well, and maybe could best follow the story of the two stuffed animals rabbits I had on my lap. The rabbits were the Brainspot.

Many kids jumped up and moved around, looking for a safe place. I can remember that most of them wanted to be close to their caretakers and wanted to be cuddled by them.

Then I started to tell a resource story, in which one rabbit ran away and that the grown-ups would take care of it, as they would do for the person who ran away that day. Forming these words into a resource fairy tale gave the kids the feeling that they were not responsible for what happened and took away potential feelings of guilt and shame.

Having them sit in special places might have enhanced the resource feeling in connection with the fairy tale. At least I had the impression that at the end of the day, the children would be able to go to bed calmly again!

ENLARGING BRAINSPOTTING TREATMENTS – ASKING FOR ADDITIONAL HELP

We all have cases where we get stuck as professionals. Besides allowing us to ask colleagues for help and advice in the form of consultations, it is sometimes important to integrate helping systems into a treatment.

Depending on the place where you live, there might be helping organizations, friends, or family persons." Regardless of where you are, it is well worth it to show our clients that we are capable of asking for further help if needed instead of going into our own flight, fight, or freeze modus during treatments.

Remember the little boy from the children's home who mentioned: "I could also be like a swimming duck, asking for help instead of attacking like a crocodile!" For me, and for all of us, he is a great example of how difficulties can be managed!

CHAPTER 4

SPREADING BRAINSPOTTING SEEDS AMONG YOUNG ONES

I am full of gratitude for your company on the Brainspotting Journey with children and adolescents. You have accompanied me during treatment sessions, crises, resourcing and even expanding. You followed in the tail of the comet, always having the head of the comet in your visual and emotional field. You allowed yourself to be uncertain and out of that might have developed your own great ideas for dealing with young clients. Thank you for all that.

Regardless of your working area, hopefully, I have encouraged you with the spontaneity, the intuition, the joy, and the power Brainspotting allows while treating the young ones or the child in each of our clients.

Whenever you discovered something interesting, need support, or you are curious about a training "Brainspotting with Children and Adolescents" or a consultation group, feel free to contact me by email at brainspottingkids@gmail.com or go to the website: www.brainspotting-kids.com

When you go out and use Brainspotting, I am sure your clients will teach you much more than I could pack into this book. In the sense of the open model of Brainspotting and the rich fantasies young ones offer, I hope you will collect a "treasure trove" of Brainspotting experiences. It does not matter if you serve as first aid in stormy times or if you are there when the storm is over. Stepping in their world, being there, and living Brainspotting in your role as a professional is what the young ones love and take advantage of, therefore, creating healing. Being yourself or your courageous inner child and enjoying the possibility to "Brainspot" is a wonderful way to spread the seeds of Brainspotting.

More Information about Brainspotting Trainings:

Brainspotting is steadily developing! Currently, Phase 1 and Phase 2 trainings as basic Brainspotting education are offered in many places around the world. You find them on www.brainspotting.com. In addition, many specialty Brainspotting trainings have been approved by Dr. Grand. I am proud to name them here, knowing that there will be more soon. Isn't it a great technique that develops in so many directions?

Brainspotting with Children and Adolescents
Mag. Monika Baumann (Austria)
Co-Created with Dr. Martha Jacobi (United States)
Visit: www.brainspotting-kids.com & www.varipets.com

**Brainspotting with Children, Adolescents
and Adult Child Parts
(Advanced Training Coming Soon)**
Mag. Monika Baumann (Austria),
www.brainspotting-kids.com

**Brain Science to Inform Your Brainspotting
Practice/AKA Animal Brain Gone Wild!**
Deb Antinori, MA, LPC, NCC, RDT, FT (United States)

Brainspotting-Couples Coregulating (BSP-CC)
Cherie Lindberg, LPC, NCC (United States)

Brainspotting and Addictions and The Hero's Journey
Roby Abeles, PsyD (Australia)

Brainspotting and Consciousness: Exploring the "Impossible" (Coming in 2022)
Christine Ranck, PhD, LCSW (United States)

Brainspotting & Parts Work
Cynthia Schwartzberg, LCSE and Cherie Lindberg, LPC, NCC (United States)

Brainspotting and Spirituality, Religion, and Contemplative Practice
The Rev. Martha S. Jacobi, PhD, LCSW-R (United States)

Critical Thinking in Brainspotting Theory, Practice, & Research
The Rev. Martha S. Jacobi, PhD, LCSW-R (United States)

Connecting the Rainbow: Brainspotting to Heal Perinatal Trauma
Jana Glass, LPC, PMH-C,
MAC, BC-TMH (United States)

Brainspotting with Adoption
Specialty Training and the Constellation
Set-ups for Brainspotting
Brooke Randolph, LMHC (United States)

Dissociation and Brainspotting
The setting of the frame in dissociation
according to Pierre Janet
Bernard Mayer and Françoise Pasqualin Dis (France)

Expansion Brainspotting Specialty Training
Lisa Larson, LMFT (United States)

Holographic Brainspotting: Explore the scientific mysteries behind Brainspotting's efficacy and expand your consciousness
Christine Ranck, PhD, LCSW (United States)

ImageSpotting
Cynthia Schwartzberg, LCSE (United States)

Going for the Roots: Developmental Trauma Focused Brainspotting
Steve Sawyer, LCSW, CSAC (United States)

From Freeze to Thaw: Unlocking Trauma in the Body with Brainspotting
Serene Calkins, P.T. (United States) and
Mary Jane O'Rourke, LCSW, LMT (United States)

From Freeze to Thaw: The Next Level
Serene Calkins, P.T. (United States) and
Mary Jane O'Rourke, LCSW, LMT (United States)
Coming Soon!

Limbic-Countertransference: Enhancing Attunement
Cynthia Schwartzberg, LCSE and
Cherie Lindberg, LPC, NCC (United States)

On Point Performance Neuro Training LLC
Paige E. Roberts, LCSW, LICSW, CLT, CBP, CBHP
(United States)

Revolutionizing Your Intake & Treatment Plan Process
Lisa Larson, LMFT (United States)

Self-Spotting: Focused Mindfulness Meditation Workshop
Cynthia Schwartzberg, LCSE (United States)

Utilizing Ego State Therapy to Enhance BSP Outcomes;
Embroidering with Multidimensional Threads
Susan Pinco, PhD, LCSW-R, CCR (United States)

Working Inside and Outside the BSP Window of Tolerance
Susan Pinco, PhD, LCSW-R, CCR (United States)

References

Anderegg, J. (n.d.). Effective treatments for generalized anxiety disorder. C/MúsicoJosé Mendez 6, 03110 Alicante, Spain: Institute Anderegg.

Baumann. (2019). PowerPoint presentation from a three-day "Brainspotting for kids and adolescents" training. Paraguay.

Baumann, M., & Jacobi, M. (2017, 03). Brainspotting mit Kindern und Jugendlichen. Zeitschrift für Psychotraumatologie und ihre Anwendungen, Brainspotting.

Baumann, M., & Jacobi, M. (2018). Brainspotting Kids. Retrieved from www.brainspotting-kids.com

Baumann, M., & Jacobi, M. (2018). Brainspotting with children and adolescents. In W. G. Ed., The power of Brainspotting (pp. 155-170). Munich, Germany: Assanger.

Baumann, M., & Jacobi, M. (2019). Brainspotting with kids and adolescents. Manual for Training, PowerPoint image. Austria.

Baumann, M., Sulek, M., & M., T. (2020, 2 21). YouTube. Retrieved from Telehealth treatments with kids and adolescents in times of Covid 19: https://youtu.be/a3syJDcBLYo

Brandt. (2018). Parts work. Psychology Today.

Bryson, S. (2011). The whole brain child. New York: Bantam Books.

Chapman. (2014). Neurobiologically informed trauma therapy with children, 6 adolescents. NY: online Trauma Counseling.

Corrigan, D. G. (2015). Brainspotting: Sustained attention, spinothalamic tracts, thalamocortical processing and the healing of adaptive orientation truncated by traumatic experience. U.K: Elsevier.

Distribution Committee of the Sandy Hook School Support, F. (2016). Report of findings from the community survey, September 2016.

E. Epel, P. J. (2011, March 15). Can meditation slow the rate of cellular aging? Cognitive stress, mindfulness, and telomeres. HHS Public Access.

Ende, M. (2015). Jim Knopf und Lukas der Lokomotivführer. Stuttgart: Thienemann.

Gendlin, E. (1976). Focusing. Chicago: Northwestern University Press.

Grand, C. (2013). Brainspotting: Recruiting the midbrain for accessing and healing sensorimotor memories of traumatic activation. . UK: Elsevier

Grand, D. (2013). Brainspotting: The revolutionary new therapy for rapid and effective change. New York: Sound True.

Grand, D. (n.d.). Brainspotting Phase 1. PowerPoint Image: Brainspotting Phase 1. NY: Grand.

Grand, D. (n.d.). Brainspotting Phase1. PowerPoint image of Brainspotting Training, Phase 1. New York: Grand.

Grand, D. (n.d.). Phase 2 Training Manual. New York: Grand.

Grand, D., & Goldberg, A. (2011). This is your brain on sports: Beating blocks, slumps and performance anxiety for good. NY: Dog Ear Publishing.

Grimm, G. &. (1812). Kinder und Hausmärchen. Deutschland: Brüder Grimm.

Grixti, D. (2015). Brainspotting with young people: an adventure into the mind. U.K: Sattva.

Health, H. (2020, July 6). Understanding the stress response, chronic activation of this survival mechanism impairs health. Harvard Health Publishing.

Hensch, B. (2012, August 29). Re-opening windows: Manipulating critical periods for brain development. Cerebrum.

Hildebrand A., G. D. (2014, 2017). A preliminary study of the efficacy of Brainspotting: A new approach for the treatment of post traumatic stress disorder. Institute of Psychology, Friedrich Alexander University Erlangen, Nürnberg: Mediterranean Journal of Clinical Psychology.

Levine, K. (2007). Trauma through a child's eyes. Berkley, California: North Atlantic Books.

Monika, B. (2018). Varipets. Retrieved from www.varipets.com

Monte, D. D. (2020, 10 21). Dr. Dr. Damir del Monte. Retrieved from https://www.damirdelmonte.de/en/home.html

Newton Sandy Hook Community Foundation, I. (2016). Report of findings from the community survey. Newton, Sandy Hook, Connecticut: School Support Fund Distribution Committee.

Porges, S. (2017, March 31). Brain-body Connections. Neuroscience.

Randolph, B. (2020). http://brooke-randolph.com/Blog/4_Types_of_Music_Used_in_Therapy?fbclid=IwAR33amD-wsJ8CbGQa2AgHQaZ20InoQb8moe0RZm7uvtDtE-FYW87DHaf0ASOM. Website.

Schwartz, H. (2018). Systemische Therapie mit der inneren Familie. Klett-Cotta.

Shonkoff. (2019). The toxic stress of early childhood adversity: Rethinking health and education policy. Boston: YouTube.

Siegel, D. (2010). Mindsight. The new science of personal transformation. New York: Bantam Book, Random House.

Souza, S. (2020). Retrieved from gettoknowme: www.salenesouza.com/gettoknowme

Thun, S. v. (1998). Miteinander Reden. Hamburg: rowohlt.

Watkins, W. &. (1997). EgoStates. Theory and therapy. New York: W.W. Norton & Company.

Wikipedia. (n.d.). Definition of trauma. Retrieved from https://de.wikipedia.org/wiki/Trauma_(Psychologie)

Wolpe. (1969). The practice of behaviour therapy. NY: Pergamon Press.

Lightning Source UK Ltd.
Milton Keynes UK
UKHW020810091022
410146UK00007B/45